Graham Greene: A Descriptive Catalog

GRAHAM GREENE
A Descriptive Catalog

ROBERT H. MILLER

Foreword by Harvey Curtis Webster

THE UNIVERSITY PRESS OF KENTUCKY

Library of Congress Cataloging in Publication Data

Miller, Robert Henry, 1938-
Graham Greene: a descriptive catalog.

Bibliography: p.
Includes index.
1. Greene, Graham, 1904-   —Bibliography—
First editions—Catalogs. 2. Louisville, Ky.
University. Library.—Catalogs.
Z8368.987.M54 [PR6013.R44]   016   77-92925
ISBN 0-8131-1383-0

Scholarly publisher for the Commonwealth
serving Berea College, Centre College of Kentucky,
Eastern Kentucky University, The Filson Club,
Georgetown College, Kentucky Historical Society,
Kentucky State University, Morehead State University,
Murray State University, Northern Kentucky University,
Transylvania University, University of Kentucky,
University of Louisville, and Western Kentucky University.

Editorial and Sales Offices: Lexington, Kentucky 40506

FOR
Jeremiah P. Starling

CONTENTS

Foreword

To CALL GRAHAM GREENE preeminent among modern writers would be as foolish as to say he is not. He does not see life steadily or whole, but he does see it as intensely as any writer in the twentieth century (there are no writers, as I see it now, who do this better than he does).

What can be said with certainty is that he sees the heart of darkness in all his characters (except for some of those in what he calls his entertainments) and the darkened plain of the modern world, which has abused itself with wars, poverty, and prejudice. With a few exceptions, he presents his vision with a craft few writers have equaled in any time. It is difficult to presume a future that would neglect *The Man Within, Brighton Rock, The Power and the Glory, The Quiet American, The End of the Affair* (my favorite and William Faulkner's) or even *The Ministry of Fear* or *Travels with My Aunt*. It is difficult to presume a future that would not wish to know all his works, his short stories, his autobiographical writings, his books about the Africa and the Mexico that affected him. Bound by time and prejudice, I believe his work, all of it, will long endure, that the best of it will endure as long as man will.

Robert Miller, a distinguished bibliographer, critic, and teacher of modern literature as well as of the earlier literature we still believe to be relevant, has compiled a catalog of Graham Greene's books which he modestly calls a contribution to a definitive bibliography. That it may be, but I can think of no other man who knows, has recorded, and has described Graham Greene's total work as completely in all its conscientious variations and all its amplitude.

HARVEY CURTIS WEBSTER

PREFACE

I BEGAN TO COLLECT Graham Greene's books during my graduate student days at Ohio State University, where I was introduced to "modern firsts" in a bibliography course taught by Matthew J. Bruccoli, now of the University of South Carolina. I had always been a reader of the novels and "entertainments," and fortunately the prices of Greene firsts were well within reach. The collection grew, with a commitment of a few dollars here and there. In 1968 I took a position at the University of Louisville; the books moved with me to my new home and there the collection continued to expand. By 1970 it consisted of over 180 items. Arrangements were made for its sale to the university through the efforts of Wayne Yenawine, then Director of Libraries. It is now housed in the John L. Patterson Room of the university library and has continued to grow modestly, to the point where it is sufficiently complete to merit a published catalog.

Had I the means and opportunity I should write a long chapter devoted to remembering and acknowledging the many persons who in one way or another assisted me in my efforts. This small token of my indebtedness must suffice, however, in lieu of some more splendid ornament.

I would like to thank especially my colleagues in the English Department and the College of Arts and Sciences for the grant of funds and released time from teaching duties, which enabled me to bring my work to completion.

I owe a debt to kind, patient, and knowledgeable book dealers, especially to Marguerite Cohn of House of Books, Ltd., to the late Lew D. Feldman of the House of El Dieff, to the firms of Bertram Rota, Ltd., and Leon Drucker of London, to Blackwell's of Oxford, and to the late Herbert F. West. To Eugene Higgins, William Gormley, and Donald Gallup, who have collected Greene titles far longer than I have, I am most grateful for shared knowledge.

I am especially indebted to the Humanities Research Center of the University of Texas, Austin, for their generosity in allowing me access to their splendid Greene collection, to the Lilly Library, Indiana University, for their many kindnesses, to the Rare Book Library of Pennsylvania State University, to the Library of Congress, and to the British Library.

I am very much in the debt of John Demos, Dean of University Libraries, University of Louisville, for his encouragement of my efforts and for his invaluable assistance in seeking support for publication. I wish to thank George McWhorter, Curator of Rare Books and Special Collections, University of Louisville, and his staff for their generous assistance.

Kathleen Santamassino provided much needed assistance by checking collations, typing, proofreading, and conducting research. For her skillful, intelligent cooperation and patience I am indeed most grateful.

To E. R. Hagemann, my compatriot in matters bibliographical, I owe a special debt for invaluable advice on technical matters of description and for a pleasant afternoon spent going over my embarrassingly numerous mistakes.

But my deepest obligation is to Jeremiah P. Starling, chairman, colleague, book lover, and friend. He caused this study to come into being. It is really his book, from its conception to its completion.

And lastly, my long overdue thanks to Matthew Bruccoli for getting me started.

R. H. M.

INTRODUCTION

IN RECENT YEARS Graham Greene's reputation as a major novelist has risen markedly. This growing interest has been reflected not only in the ever-multiplying body of Greene criticism but also in the number of individuals and libraries which have begun to develop Greene collections and in the sharp rise in prices of first editions of his works, especially those published before 1942. In 1965 a first edition of his first novel, *The Man Within*, in fine condition in a dust jacket, sold for about seventeen dollars, and a copy of his first book, *Babbling April*, brought about a hundred dollars. Today *The Man Within* regularly brings well over one hundred fifty dollars, and *Babbling April* in jacket sells for over three hundred dollars. Any "quantification" or "valuation" of Greene's reputation is frivolous, of course, but the prices do indicate that there has been a sudden recent focusing of interest on Greene.

To some extent the rise can be tied to two important sales of Greene's books and manuscripts. The first was the purchase of a large collection of manuscript material at Sotheby's, on 11 May 1964, by the House of El Dieff.[1] This material now forms the basis of the excellent Greene collection at the Humanities Research Center, University of Texas, Austin. The second was the sale of John Hayward's library at Sotheby's on 12 July 1966, which included virtually every Greene title published up to that time, many of the items being presentation copies from Greene to his good friend John Hayward.[2] By today's standards the prices paid at that auction do not seem especially high, but by the standards of 1966 they were out of the ordinary. Since that time, of course, they have continued to rise, at first precipitously and of late, modestly but insistently.

Because his career has been so extensive and varied, Greene naturally appeals to the collector. In its breadth his professional career rivals that of any writer of this century; and locating copies of Greene "firsts" can be a challenging task, for it takes one into the realms of travel literature, autobiography, literary criticism, the essay, poetry, drama, film, film criticism, the detective novel, the "thriller," juveniles, and novels of several different kinds. There is perhaps also a certain attraction to collecting a writer who is himself an assiduous and enterprising collector, as Greene has proved to be in his quest for copies of nineteenth-century detective fiction.[3] Some of his titles are almost impossible to find. The early travel books, *Journey without Maps* and *The Lawless Roads*, are quite rare, the juveniles almost never come on the market, and the two suppressed novels, *The Name of Action* and *Rumour at Nightfall*, are seldom offered, and then rarely in dust jacket. The "manufactured rarities," particularly the later "limited edition" items, continue to be offered with some regularity, with the exception of *The Bear Fell Free*, which has become scarce. Like Neil Brennan, I too have been unable to acquire or even locate a copy of Greene's history of the Azores, issued by the British government in only twelve copies.[4] Nor have I been able to locate copies of two privately issued items, *After Two Years* and *For Christmas*, which Greene informs me do exist but "are purely private and not for sale."[5] But over the years, through good fortune or the kindness of bookmen who are always looking out for the needs of the impecunious amateur, both the contrivedly scarce and the truly scarce items have managed to find their way into the collection. While it may lack depth in certain titles and though it cannot possibly boast of manuscript treasures and association copies to rival those of the University of Texas, it is surprisingly thorough, as this catalog will testify, and the books, as any visitor knows, are in remarkably fine condition.

The foundation of good literary scholarship is solid textual scholarship; the foundation of solid textual scholarship, careful bibliographical scholarship. All depend on each other and come to fruition in the judicious, informed unfolding of the intricacies of meaning and layers of signification that are the concern of the sensitive critic. Greene stands much in need of all three, and it is my hope that this catalog will be the beginning of an effort to learn more about the physical books that have been the product of his writing career. It is a minimal undertaking but an important one. I am also of the opinion that the best and most durable bibliographies are those that describe actual copies, and so I have attempted to present just such a bibliography of a good working collection. To the collector this catalog provides significant information about the physical nature of a given book, its title page, binding, format, etc. To the bibliographer it provides a thorough and detailed list that will function as a working bibliography in lieu of a more complete one; and for the compilers of the definitive Greene bibliography, this catalog offers a modest but I hope very useful beginning for such a mammoth undertaking. To the textual scholar, most importantly perhaps, the catalog locates copies of significance, particularly proof copies and advance review copies (to my knowledge the largest institutional collection of such items) that will have to be consulted in future attempts to study the texts of Greene's works. What little I know at the moment convinces me that the "Greene text" will present many problems. The recent study of Philip Stratford of *The Heart of the Matter*, in *Studies in Bibliography*, 31 (1978), should prove to us all that no effort at cataloging and examining these books will go unrewarded. For the scholar and reader this catalog provides the first public printed listing of Greene titles in a given collection, which are available for their consultation and use. Anyone wishing to use the collection may do so by writing the Curator of Rare Books and Special Collections, Main Library, University of Louisville.

This catalog describes letters, radio scripts, pamphlets, and first English and American editions of works by Greene in the collection at the University of Louisville. In a few instances it also lists subsequent editions of some importance and scarcity. It does not list books in part by Greene, though the collection's holdings of those items are virtually complete. All descriptions are of copies in the collection in their present state. The system of description is based on that of Fredson Bowers, *Principles of Bibliographical Description* (Princeton: Princeton University Press, 1949), chapter 12, with some minor modifications. All descriptions are arranged within respective sections chronologically by title, though I have made no effort to establish exact dates of publication, nor have I attempted to establish exactly the bibliographical nature of each item, as to edition, printing, issue, or state. This catalog is primarily a bibliography of actual copies.

Each entry contains four basic parts: transcription of title page, collation of gatherings and pagination, description of contents, and description of binding and dust jacket. In some instances I have included brief notes containing bibliographical information based on my researches in other collections. If any edition has been listed in Neil Brennan's bibliography in *Graham Greene: Some Critical Considerations* (Lexington: University of Kentucky Press, 1963), pp. 245-76, I have also referenced the item accordingly, simply as "Brennan [no.]." The four parts to each entry deserve fuller explanation.

1) *Transcription of title page.* Each title page is given in line-by-line form, each line separated by a vertical bar. Type style is indicated only in general terms; no effort is made to indicate fonts or the various display faces used frequently on title pages of the Viking editions. Publishers' ornaments, devices, and the like are indicated and described within brackets, with their dimensions given, vertical first, then horizontal.

2) *Collation of gatherings and pagination.* The size of the book is indicated in parentheses, the measurements being the vertical and horizontal dimensions of the right-hand leaf of the conjugate pair at the center of the first gathering of a given volume. Collation of gatherings is given, with unsigned gatherings indicated in italic type. Pagination is given in the same manner. I have not attempted to analyze internal arabic pagination, so that a set of arabic pagination listed as "9-108," for example, may contain within it any number of pages that do not carry page numbers.

3) *Description of contents.* Every effort has been made to describe all contents fully, though some abbreviation has been necessary for reasons of space. All pages considered integral to the book (in some rare instances endpapers fall into this category) are noted as to contents. Terminology employed is that of John Carter, *ABC for Book Collectors*, 5th ed. (New York: Knopf, 1972).

4) *Description of binding and dust jacket.* Descriptions of bindings and jackets are always shaped by the eye of the beholder, and these efforts are no exception, but I have attempted

to describe materials, graphics, pictorial designs, and colors as faithfully as possible. Because of the effects of age on binding and jacket colors, especially in the earlier copies, I have abandoned reluctantly any effort to identify colors by specific ISCC-NBS centroid chip numbers, but I have in most cases relied on the descriptive terminology of that system.[6] If an entry contains no description of a dust jacket, it is understood that the copy described carries no jacket. Where a book is known to have been issued without a dust jacket, that information is given.

I shall be very grateful for any additions or corrections to this catalog. May they be few, but if they be not, they will be welcome nonetheless.

It is my hope that this effort will stimulate interest in the university's collection and will contribute in some small way to the efforts of Neil Brennan, A. R. Redway, and others in their work on a definitive bibliography of all Greene's writings, a monumental undertaking indeed. I am sure this contribution will be only the first in a number of efforts to bring together our knowledge of the composition and publication of Greene's books, articles, and reviews.

———— •·• ◄————

1. *American Book-Prices Current*, 1963-64, pp. 809-11.
2. *Catalogue of Nineteenth Century and Modern First Editions*, 12 July 1966, lots 77-110.
3. The catalog of this collection is essential to a student of the genre. See *Victorian Detective Fiction*, ed. Eric Osborne (London: Bodley Head, 1966), item 48a of this bibliography.
4. "Bibliography," in *Graham Greene: Some Critical Considerations*, ed. R. O. Evans (Lexington: University of Kentucky Press, 1963), p. 246.
5. Brennan 21 and 26, respectively. Letter of 14 May 1966.
6. A brief description of the color system is given in Philip Gaskell, *A New Introduction to Bibliography* (Oxford: Clarendon Press, 1972), pp. 237-39. A fuller account is G. Thomas Tanselle's article, "A System of Color Identification for Bibliographical Description," *Studies in Bibliography*, 20 (1967), 203-34.

Bibliographies Consulted

"A Bibliography of Graham Greene." *Marginalia*, 2 (April 1951), 16-19 [mimeograph].

Boardman, Gwenn R. *Graham Greene: The Aesthetics of Exploration.* Gainesville: University of Florida Press, 1971, pp. 187-98.

Brennan, Neil. "Bibliography." *Graham Greene: Some Critical Considerations.* Ed. R. O. Evans. Lexington: University of Kentucky Press, 1963, pp. 245-76.

"Graham Greene." *New Cambridge Bibliography of English Literature,* IV (Cambridge: Cambridge University Press, 1972), 503-12.

Hargreaves, Phylis. "Graham Greene: A Selected Bibliography." *Modern Fiction Studies,* 3 (1957), 269-80.

Vann, J. Don. *Graham Greene: A Checklist of Criticism.* Kent, Ohio: Kent State University Press, 1970.

A definitive bibliography has been in preparation for some years now, under the direction of Neil Brennan and A. R. Redway.

The Descriptive Catalog

LETTERS

1. Autograph Letter, signed, with envelope. From GG to R. N. Green-Armytage, dated 23 May [1933], one leaf, two pages. On his mother-in-law's death, explaining why he and his wife were unable to attend the funeral. The date "1933" appears in the envelope's postmark; it is penciled in the upper right corner of the first page of the letter, in another hand.

2. Typed Letter, signed, with envelope. From GG to Robert Miller, dated from Paris 14 May 1966, one page. Brief comments on the English poet Royall Snow, on the two suppressed novels, *The Name of Action* and *Rumour at Nightfall*, on *Babbling April*, and on two privately printed items, *After Two Years* and *For Christmas* (Brennan 21 and 26).

RADIO SCRIPTS

3. Radio script of *The Third Man*, mimeographed, for "The Theatre Guild on the Air," marked "FINAL REHEARSAL | 1–6–51."

   (279 x 215 mm.) Erratically paged, consisting of 101 leaves. Stapled in upper left corner.

4. Radio script of *The Fallen Idol*, mimeographed, for "The Theatre Guild on the Air," marked "FINAL REHEARSAL | 4/1/51."

   (279 x 215 mm.) Erratically paged, consisting of 102 leaves. Stapled in upper left corner.

PAMPHLET

5. [upper half, color reproduction of Caffè painting] | NINO CAFFÈ | KNOEDLER | *14 East 57 Th Street* | NEW YORK

   (159 x 234 mm.) *i–iv.*

   Stiff paper two-leaf folded pamphlet, distributed at the Caffè exhibit, December 1953. Greene's appreciation appears on pp.

ii–iii; iv, colophon: *PRINTED IN ITALY* | INSTITUTO GRAFICO TIBERINO—VIA GAETA 14—ROMA.

Brennan 31.

BOOKS

6. *Babbling April*

a. BABBLING APRIL | BY GRAHAM GREENE | OXFORD: BASIL BLACKWELL | 1925

(192 x 129 mm.) a^4 b–c^8; *i–viii,* 1–32.

Contents: *i,* title page; *ii,* colophon: "PRINTED AND MADE IN GREAT BRITAIN | AT THE SHAKESPEARE HEAD PRESS | STRATFORD-UPON-AVON"; *iii,* quote from Edna St. Vincent Millay's "Spring," from *Second April; iv,* dedication to his father and mother; *v,* note on previous appearance of poems; *vi,* blank; *vii,* table of contents; *viii,* blank; 1–32, text.

Binding: Pale purplish-blue paper boards, with the following printed in blue ink on the front board: "Babbling April | Graham Greene | [ornament: solid blue leaf]." Dust jacket: Gray textured paper, with the following printed in black on the front cover: "Babbling April | Graham Greene | [ornament: solid black leaf] | Oxford | Basil Blackwell · Broad Street | *Price 4 s. 6 d. net.*" Rear cover carries advertisements for *Oxford Poetry 1924* and *Eighty Poems.*

Note: According to Blackwell's, *Babbling April* was published in a limited edition of 500 copies, 302 of which were bound. Forty review copies were sent out on 30 April 1925, twelve copies were sent to the author on 13 May, and the book was formally published on 18 May. On 1 June 1934, "200 quires" were withdrawn from stock and scrapped, "quires" referring to unbound individual copies rather than to separate gatherings of copies (letters from P. Fenemore, Antiquarian Department, Blackwell's, of 17 August 1970 and 1 September 1976). This copy belonged to Royall Snow, who reviewed it for *Poetry Magazine,* 29

(May 1926), 112–14, with his signature on the recto of
the front free endpaper. Snow and Greene were at Oxford
at the same time.

Brennan 1.

7. *The Man Within*

a. THE MAN WITHIN | BY | GRAHAM GREENE | [or-
nament, 3 mm.: parallelogram] | "There's another man
within me | that's angry with me." | SIR THOMAS
BROWNE. | [publisher's device: Heinemann windmill]
| [double taper rule] | LONDON: WILLIAM HEINE-
MANN LTD

(185 x 120 mm.) *A* B–Y⁸; *i–xii*, 1–354 *355–356*.

Contents: *i–ii*, blank; *iii*, half-title; *iv*, list of new and recent
fiction; *v*, title page; *vi*, copyright page: "First published
1929"; *vii*, dedication to his wife, with a six-line quote from
Thomas Hardy; *viii*, blank; *ix*, table of contents; *x*, blank;
xi, "PART I"; *xii*, blank; 1–354, text; *355–356*, blank.

Binding: Black cloth with gold lettering on the spine. Front
board carries single-rule, blind-stamped border. Rear board
carries Heinemann windmill blind-stamped in lower right
corner. Dust jacket: Pale yellowish-white paper with the
following on its front cover: "[within a double frame of
blue triangular ornaments in blue ink] THE | MAN
WITHIN | GRAHAM GREENE." Rear cover carries ad-
vertisements for other Heinemann titles.

Note: Pickford Waller's copy, with his bookplate on the
front pastedown endpaper. By Greene's accounting, total
sales of this edition numbered 8,000 copies, of which 2,500
copies constituted the first printing (*A Sort of Life* [Lon-
don: Bodley Head, 1971], pp. 192, 215).

Brennan 2.

b. [all the following in black within a green octagonal three-
rule frame] THE | MAN | WITHIN | BY GRAHAM
GREENE | [publisher's device: dolphin and anchor within
octagonal frame, in green] | *"There's another man within*

me | *that's angry with me."* | *Sir Thomas Browne.* | DOUBLEDAY, DORAN & COMPANY, INC. | GARDEN CITY, NEW YORK | *MCMXXIX*

(190 x 127 mm.) 1^8 $(1_1+\chi^2)$ $2-20^8$; *i–vi, 1–2 3–316 317–318.*

Contents: *i–ii*, blank; *iii*, half-title; *iv*, brief profile of GG; *v*, title page; *vi*, copyright page; *1–316*, text; *317–318*, blank.

Binding: Green cloth, with dark green cloth spine, gold lettering on spine. Top edges stained green; green endpapers. Fore edges uncut.

Brennan 2.

8. *The Name of Action*

a. THE | NAME | OF ACTION | *by* | Graham Greene | *" . and lose the name of action."* | Hamlet | [publisher's device: Heinemann windmill] | LONDON | WILLIAM HEINEMANN LTD

(186 x 117 mm.) A $B-W^8$ X^{10}; *i–x, 1–2 3–344 345–346.*

Contents: *i–ii*, blank; *iii*, half-title; *iv*, advertisement for *The Man Within; v*, title page; *vi*, copyright page: "FIRST PUBLISHED 1930"; *vii*, dedication to Vivienne Greene with quote from Donne; *viii*, blank; *ix*, quote from T. S. Eliot and author's disclaimer; *x*, blank; *1–344*, text, with the date *"March, 1929–July, 1930"* on p. 344; *345–346*, blank.

Binding: Dark blue cloth with gold lettering on spine. Front board carries single-rule, blind-stamped border. Rear board carries Heinemann windmill blind-stamped in lower right corner. Dust jacket: Yellow paper with the following on front cover: "[all the following within two vertical lines of black triangular ornaments] The Name | of Action [title in red] | [in black] by | GRAHAM | GREENE | Author of | THE MAN WITHIN." Rear cover carries excerpts from reviews of *The Man Within.*

Note: John Hayward's copy, lot 80 of the Hayward sale at Sotheby's, 12 July 1966. This novel, along with *Rumour at Nightfall* (9a, 9b), has been suppressed by GG and exists only in the first English and American editions of 1930 and 1931 respectively. In *A Sort of Life*, GG puts the sales of *NA* at slightly over 2,000 copies (p. 199).

Brennan 3.

b. [in black] THE | NAME OF ACTION | *Graham Greene* | AUTHOR OF "THE MAN | WITHIN" | [in red: Doubleday seal, dolphin and anchor] | [in black] " . *and lose the name of action.*" HAMLET | [in red: thin double taper rule, 93 mm.] | [in black] *Doubleday, Doran & Company, Inc.* | *Garden City, New York* | MCMXXXI

(190 x 130 mm.) $1(1_1+1)$ 2–20^8; *i–x, 1–2* 3–312.

Contents: *i*, half-title; *ii*, blank; *iii*, title page; *iv*, copyright page; *v*, dedication: "FOR VIVIENNE," with a quote from John Donne; *vi*, blank; *vii*, quote from T. S. Eliot; *viii*, blank; *ix*, disclaimer; *x*, blank; *1–312*, text.

Binding: Black cloth with a blind-stamped figure of a lion in the center of the front board. Spine carries title and author's name, but lettering is too faded to allow the color to be noted. Red endpapers.

Brennan 3.

9. *Rumour at Nightfall*

a. [in red] *Rumour at* | *Nightfall* | [in black] *by Graham Greene* | [publisher's device in red: Heinemann windmill] | *London* | *William Heinemann Ltd*

(183 x 120 mm.) *A* B–F G H–S^8 T^{10}; *i–viii, 1–300*.

Contents: *i*, half-title; *ii*, list of books by GG; *iii*, title page; *iv*, copyright: "FIRST PUBLISHED 1931"; *v*, dedication to his father and mother; *vi*, blank; *vii*, quote from Thomas Traherne; *viii*, blank; *1–300*, text.

Binding: Red cloth with gold lettering on spine. Front board carries blind-stamped, four-pointed star in upper right corner, with five rays emanating outward. Rear board carries Heinemann windmill blind-stamped in lower right corner.

Note: This novel exists only in this edition and the first American edition noted below. GG puts the sale of this edition at 1,200 copies (*A Sort of Life*, p. 207).

Brennan 4.

b. RUMOUR AT NIGHTFALL | Graham Greene | [double taper rule] | [publisher's device: dolphin and anchor, in white in a solid red rectangle] | Doubleday, Doran & Company, Inc. | Garden City 1932 New York

(190 x 130 mm.) 1^8 (1_1+1) $2-18^8$ 19^4 20^8; *i–xii, 1–299 300–302.*

Contents: *i–ii*, blank; *iii*, half-title; *iv*, advertisement; *v*, title page; *vi*, copyright page; *vii*, dedication to his father and mother; *viii*, blank; *ix*, quote from Thomas Traherne; *x*, blank; *xi*, "PART I"; *xii*, blank; *1–299*, text; *300–302*, blank.

Binding: Black cloth with red cloth spine carrying black chevronlike design and red lettering. Top edges stained red; red endpapers. Fore edges uncut.

Brennan 4.

10. *Stamboul Train*

a. [double rule] | STAMBOUL TRAIN | BY | GRAHAM GREENE | [double rule] | [publisher's device: Heinemann windmill] | LONDON | WILLIAM HEINEMANN LTD | [double rule]

(178 x 116 mm.) *A* B–U⁸; *i–xii, 1–2 3–307 308.*

Contents: *i–ii*, blank; *iii*, half-title; *iv*, list of GG's three previously published novels; *v*, title page; *vi*, copyright page: "FIRST PUBLISHED 1932"; *vii*, dedication to his wife; *viii*, blank; *ix*, quote from George Santayana; *x*, blank; *xi*, table of contents; *xii*, blank; *1–307*, text; *308*, blank.

Binding: Black cloth with gold lettering on spine. Front board carries single-rule, blind-stamped border. Rear board carries Heinemann windmill blind-stamped in lower right corner. Dust jacket: Front cover carries a multicolor pictorial representation of the Stamboul Train descending from upper left to lower right across a map of Europe. Superimposed are title and author's name in white in a solid blue banner. Illustration is signed "Youngman Carter." Spine is white with blue lettering. Rear cover, white, carries an advertisement for *Rumour at Nightfall*.

Note: GG has indicated in *A Sort of Life* (London: Bodley Head, 1971), pp. 213–15, that some textual changes had to be made in the first printing to accommodate J. B. Priestley's claim that he was libeled by Greene's alleged satirical portrayal of him in the character of the popular novelist Quin Savory. A copy of the novel sold at Sotheby's (Sale 19, 5–7 May 1958, Item 863) carried a presentation inscription from GG, citing that the "first printing had to be scrapped because of a threatened libel action" (*American Book Prices Current* [1958], p. 174). Bernard Quaritch Ltd., in Catalogue 900 (1970), listed on p. 16, Item 219, a copy of *ST:* "The dust-wrapper, albeit rather torn, is most interesting in that it is apparently a trial issue without type on the back or advertisements elsewhere. There is also a bibliographical note by the publisher on the front end-paper." This copy is now in the collection of Eugene Higgins of New York. It contains the original readings before they were altered. See also R. H. Miller, "Textual Alterations in Graham Greene's *Stamboul Train*," *PBSA*, 71 (1977), 378–81.

Brennan 5.

b. *Orient Express* | BY GRAHAM GREENE | [publisher's device: two calligraphic upper-case D's, intertwined] | *1933* | [double taper rule] | *Doubleday, Doran & Company, Inc.* | GARDEN CITY, NEW YORK

(190 x 130 mm.) $1-20^8$; $i-x$, $1-2$ $3-310$.

Contents: *i*, half-title; *ii*, list of books by GG; *iii*, title page; *iv*, copyright page; *v*, dedication to his wife; *vi*, blank; *vii*, quote from Santayana; *viii*, blank; *ix*, table of contents; *x*, blank; *1–310*, text.

Binding: Red cloth with black lettering on spine. A train printed in black runs from upper third of spine diagonally across spine to lower front board. Front board shows front of engine and railroad tracks. Top edges stained red; pale yellowish-white endpapers. Fore edges uncut.

Note: No textual variants exist between the text of this copy and that of the first English edition, with respect to the section GG had to revise to meet J. B. Priestley's objections. See note on the first English edition, 10a.

Brennan 5.

11. *It's a Battlefield*

a. GRAHAM GREENE | [double rule, lower rule shorter] | IT'S A | BATTLEFIELD | [publisher's device: Heinemann windmill] | [double rule, upper rule shorter] | LONDON | WILLIAM HEINEMANN LTD

(183 x 123 mm.) *A* B–S⁸; *i–x*, 1–275 276–278.

Contents: *i–ii*, blank; *iii*, half-title; *iv*, list of books by GG; *v*, title page; *vi*, copyright: "FIRST PUBLISHED 1934"; *vii*, dedication: "FOR DAVID AND ANNE IN LONDON, | AND FOR NILS AND INGEBORG IN OSLO."; *viii*, author's disclaimer; *ix*, quote from Alexander Kinglake; *x*, blank; 1–275, text; *276–278*, blank.

Binding: Black cloth with gold lettering on spine. Rear board carries Heinemann windmill blind-stamped in lower right corner.

Brennan 6.

b. *Graham Greene* | IT'S A BATTLEFIELD | [publisher's device: two calligraphic upper-case D's, intertwined] | 1934 | [double taper rule] | *Doubleday, Doran & Company, Inc.* | GARDEN CITY, NEW YORK

(190 x 130 mm.) *1–20⁸*; *i–xiv, 1* 2–304 *305–306*.

Contents: *i–ii*, blank; *iii*, half-title; *iv*, list of books by GG; *v*, title page; *vi*, copyright page; *vii*, dedication: "FOR | DAVID AND ANNE IN LONDON, | AND FOR |

NILS AND INGEBORG | IN OSLO"; *viii*, blank; *ix*, author's disclaimer; *x*, blank; *xi*, quote from Alexander Kinglake; *xii*, blank; *xiii*, half-title; *xiv*, blank; *1–304*, text; *305–306*, blank.

Binding: Pale brownish-pink cloth with black basket weave design on spine and title in black diagonal label. Top edges stained black. Fore edges uncut. Dust jacket: Front cover carries a photographic collage of [from left to right] a man in white-tie dress, a reclining woman positioned upside down and wearing a silk dress, and a newsboy. Superimposed at top in white and gold lettering are title and author's name. The left side of the collage is reproduced on spine. Rear cover carries a photo of GG and a brief profile.

Brennan 6.

c. *GRAHAM GREENE* | [within a single-rule frame extending onto p. *ii*] | *IT'S A BATTLEFIELD* | *The Viking Press • New York*

(201 x 134 mm.) *1–7*[16]; *i–iv* v–viii *ix–x*, 1–214.

Contents: *i*, half-title; *ii*, list of books by GG; *iii*, title page; *iv*, copyright: "First published in 1934 | Reissued in 1962 by The Viking Press, Inc."; v–viii, "Introduction"; *ix*, quote from Alexander Kinglake; *x*, blank; 1–214, text.

Binding: Medium blue cloth with pale green lettering on spine. Front cover carries geometrical flower design blindstamped in lower right corner. Top edges stained pale green; black endpapers. Dust jacket: Front cover and spine are black. Front cover, lettered in white, carries geometrical flower in black, blue, pale and dark green, and white, in lower two-thirds. Spine is lettered in white, blue, and pale green. Rear cover, white, carries a quote from GG's introduction to the novel.

Note: A new edition in a revised text.

12. *The Bear Fell Free*

a. THE GRAYSON BOOKS | Edited by *JOHN HACK-NEY* | [double rule, lower rule bold] | *The* | *Bear Fell* |

Free | • | Graham | Greene | [double rule, upper rule bold] | GRAYSON & GRAYSON | LONDON: MDCCCCXXXV

(218 x 143 mm.) *A* B–E⁴; *1–40*.

Contents: *1–2*, blank; *3*, half-title; *4*, blank; *5*, "285 copies only of this first | edition of THE BEAR FELL | FREE by *GRAHAM GREENE* | have been printed: 250 of | these, numbered, and signed | by the author, are for sale. | This is number 184 | [signed] Graham Greene"; *6*, blank; *7*, title page; *8*, blank; *9*, quotation from Weyl; *10–11*, blank; *12*, line drawing; *13–30*, text; *31–32*, blank; *33*, list of GG's other works; *34*, blank; *35*, credit to the illustrator Joy Lloyd; *36*, blank; *37*, colophon, "The Grayson Books *edited by* John Hackney | *are published by* Grayson & Grayson Ltd., | Curzon Street, Mayfair, London, *and printed* | *and made by* The Garden City Press | Ltd., Letchworth, Herts. *A. D.* mdccccxxxv."; *38–40*, blank.

Binding: Brown cloth. Front board carries a gold design, with author's name and title in gold. Rear board carries a floral ornament with the initials GG in gold. Top edges stained brown; endpapers contain monogram and ornaments in brown ink. Fore edges uncut.

Note: The Grayson Books comprised a series of twelve titles, edited by John Hackney, and published in 1935 in a limited edition of 285 copies each. The GG title is the most sought after (Bertram Rota Ltd., *125 Rare and Interesting Modern Books 1846–1966* [Summer 1970], Catalogue 166, pp. 14–15).

Brennan 7.

b. Another copy, identical to 12a. This copy is No. 237.

13. *England Made Me*
    a. ENGLAND MADE ME | *A NOVEL* | BY | GRAHAM GREENE | [floral ornament, 5 x 4 mm.] | [publisher's device: Heinemann windmill] | [rule] | WILLIAM HEINEMANN LTD | LONDON : : TORONTO

(184 x 122 mm.) *A* B–T⁸ U¹⁰; *i–x*, 1–314.

Contents: *i–ii*, blank; *iii*, half-title; *iv*, list of GG's other novels; *v*, title page; *vi*, copyright page: "FIRST PUBLISHED 1935"; *vii*, dedication to his wife, Vivien; *viii*, blank; *ix*, quote from Walt Disney's film *The Grasshopper and the Ants; x*, author's disclaimer; 1–314, text.

Binding: Red cloth with gold lettering on spine. Rear board carries Heinemann windmill blind-stamped in lower right corner.

Brennan 8.

b. THE SHIPWRECKED | A NOVEL BY | Graham Greene | NEW YORK • THE VIKING PRESS • 1953

(203 x 135 mm.) *1–8¹⁶*; *i–x*, *1–2 3–244 245–246*.

Contents: *i–ii*, blank; *iii*, half-title; *iv*, list of books by GG; *v*, title page; *vi*, copyright: "REISSUED BY THE VIKING PRESS IN JANUARY 1953"; *vii*, dedication: "TO VIVIEN"; *viii*, disclaimer; *ix*, quote from Walt Disney's *The Grasshopper and the Ants; x*, blank; *1*, half-title; *2*, blank; *3–244*, text; *245–246*, blank.

Binding: Black linen-embossed paper boards with black lettering on quarter yellow cloth spine. Top edges stained yellow. Dust jacket: Front cover and spine are purple. Front cover carries riverfront scene in black, with title at head and author's name at tail in pale green. Spine is lettered in white and pale green. Rear cover, white, carries a photo portrait of GG by Lida Moser.

Note: On the cover page of the autograph manuscript, this title is listed as an alternate, along with "The ex-patriates." Both are canceled by a single line. The manuscript is dated 16 November 1933 (U Tex Collection).

Brennan 8.

14. *The Basement Room and Other Stories*

a. Graham Greene | [double rule, lower rule bold] | THE BASEMENT | ROOM | *and other stories* | THE CRES-

SET PRESS LIMITED | 11 FITZROY SQUARE |
LONDON

(184 x 108 mm.) *A* B–L⁸; *A–B, i–vi* vii *viii, 1–2* 3–164
165–166.

Contents: *A–B*, blank; *i*, half-title; *ii*, blank; *iii*, title page;
iv, copyright page: *"First Published 1935"; v*, dedication:
"To | CHARLES EVANS"; *vi*, blank; vii, table of con-
tents; *viii*, blank; *1–165*, text; *165*, colophon: "Printed in
Great Britain by Butler & Tanner Ltd., Frome and London"; *166*, blank.

Binding: Green cloth with gold lettering on spine.

Note: Booksellers' catalogs distinguish two bindings,
green and red cloth, and assign precedence to the green
cloth binding. No other differences between these copies
exist (red-cloth copy examined: University of Texas,
Ellery Queen Collection, No. 1838).

Brennan 9.

15. *Journey without Maps*

a. JOURNEY | WITHOUT MAPS | BY | GRAHAM
GREENE | [ornament, 3 x 8 mm.: bull's head] | [pub-
lisher's device: Heinemann windmill] | [rule] | WIL-
LIAM HEINEMANN LTD | LONDON : : TO-
RONTO

(216 x 139 mm.) *A¹⁰* B–T⁸; *i–viii* ix–x *xi–xii, 1–2* 3–296.
Photographic plates inserted after pp. *ii*, 24, 36, 84, 96,
100, 104, 112, 124, 128, 140, 152, 160, 168, 180, 192, 200,
216, 220, 224, 236, 244, 256, 264.

Contents: *i*, half-title; *ii*, list of books by GG; *iii*, title
page; *iv*, copyright page: "FIRST PUBLISHED 1936";
v, dedication to his wife; *vi*, blank; *vii*, table of contents;
viii, blank; ix–x, list of illustrations; *xi*, quotes from W. H.
Auden and Oliver Wendell Holmes; *xii*, blank; *1–296*,
text.

Binding: Light olive cloth with brown lettering on spine.
Rear board carries Heinemann windmill stamped in brown

in lower right corner. Top edges stained russet; endpapers decorated with map of GG's itinerary.

Note: According to GG in his Introduction to the Collected Edition of *Stamboul Train*, this edition had to be withdrawn from publication because of a threatened libel action (*Stamboul Train* [London: Bodley Head, 1974], p. xi).

Brennan 10.

b. *Journey* | *Without Maps* | GRAHAM GREENE | [publisher's device: ship at harbor, man pointing to letters "DD" on a monument] | *Garden City   New York* | DOUBLEDAY, DORAN & COMPANY, INC. | *1936*

(200 x 138 mm.) *1–20⁸*; *i–x, 1–2 3–310.*

Contents: *i*, half-title; *ii*, list of books by GG; *iii*, title page; *iv*, copyright page; *v*, dedication to his wife; *vi*, blank; *vii*, quotes from W. H. Auden and Oliver Wendell Holmes; *viii*, blank; *ix*, table of contents; *x*, blank; *1–310*, text.

Binding: Black cloth with gold lettering on spine. Front board carries blind-stamped figure of a tribal chieftain, centered. Top edges stained russet; endpapers decorated with map of Greene's itinerary. Fore edges uncut. Dust jacket: Front cover and spine carry pictorial representation of raft being poled up a river, in brown, black, and yellow. Rear cover carries a brief printed profile of GG.

Brennan 10.

16. *A Gun for Sale*

a. GRAHAM GREENE | *This Gun For Hire* | [publisher's device: ship at harbor, man pointing to letters "DD" on a monument] | [rule] | DOUBLEDAY DORAN & COMPANY, INC. | *Garden City* 1936 *New York*

(190 x 130 mm.) *1–19⁸*; *i–viii, 1 2–293 294–296.*

Contents: *i*, synopsis of the novel; *ii*, blank; *iii*, half-title; *iv*, list of books by GG; *v*, title page; *vi*, copyright page; *vii*, half-title; *viii*, blank; *1–293*, text; *294–296*, blank.

Binding: Tan cloth with three green-stamped labels on spine. Top edges stained olive; tan endpapers. Fore edges uncut.

Brennan 11.

b. A GUN FOR SALE | AN ENTERTAINMENT | BY | GRAHAM GREENE | [ornament, 3 x 8 mm.: bull's head] | [publisher's device: Heinemann windmill] | [rule] | WILLIAM HEINEMANN LTD | LONDON : : TO-RONTO

(190 x 127 mm.) *A* B–R⁸; *i–viii*, 1–261 *262–264*.

Contents: *i–ii*, blank; *iii*, half-title; *iv*, list of books by GG; *v*, title page; *vi*, copyright page: "FIRST PUBLISHED 1936"; *vii*, half-title; *viii*, blank; 1–261, text; *262–264*, blank.

Binding: Red cloth with gold lettering on spine. Rear board carries Heinemann windmill blind-stamped in lower right corner. Red endpapers.

Brennan 11.

c. [all the following within a five-rule frame, outer rule bold] This Gun | For Hire | Graham Greene | A SU-PERIOR REPRINT | Published by | The Military Service Publishing Co. | Harrisburg, Pennsylvania

(163 x 105 mm.) Pp. *i–iv, 1* 2–216 *217–218*.

Contents: *i*, title page; *ii*, copyright: "FIRST PUB-LISHED IN THIS SERIES, JUNE, 1945"; *iii*, half-title; *iv*, blank; *1*–216, text; *217–218*, blank.

Binding: Paperback, perfect binding. Front cover is in orange, brown, and gray with a gunman in black-and-white silhouette; author's name and title are in white letters at head. Rear cover carries in orange-and-black frame a photo and brief biography of GG.

Note: Military Services Edition No. M652.

17. *Brighton Rock*

    a. *Graham Greene* | BRIGHTON ROCK | *An Entertain-*

ment | [double rule, top rule bold] | *New York* | THE VIKING PRESS | *1938*

(203 x 130 mm.) *1–23*⁸; *i–viii, 1–2 3–358 359–360.*

Contents: *i,* half-title; *ii,* list of books by GG; *iii,* title page; *iv,* copyright page: "PUBLISHED IN JUNE 1938"; *v,* quote from *The Witch of Edmonton; vi,* blank; *vii,* two notes: one on treasure hunts, one on Brighton Rock candy; *viii,* blank; *1–358,* text; *359–360,* blank.

Binding: Rose cloth with black border at head 25 mm. wide. Spine is lettered in silver; black border on the spine is edged with a silver single rule, 5 mm. wide. On front board, a black border is edged at the bottom with a silver double rule, top rule 5 mm. wide. Top edges stained black. Dust jacket: Front cover and spine carry pictorial representation of events in the novel in black outline on a blue background. Superimposed is a phonograph in black outline. Illustration is signed "Salten." Rear cover, white, carries a synopsis of the novel.

Brennan 12.

b. BRIGHTON ROCK | A NOVEL | BY | GRAHAM GREENE | [ornament, 2 x 4 mm.: parallelogram, with bottom half solid black] | [publisher's device: Heinemann windmill] | [rule] | WILLIAM HEINEMANN LTD | LONDON : : TORONTO

(190 x 125 mm.) *A* B–Y⁸; *i–vi, 1–2 3–361 362.*

Contents: *i,* half-title; *ii,* list of books by GG; *iii,* title page; *iv,* copyright: "FIRST PUBLISHED 1938"; *v,* quote from *The Witch of Edmonton; vi,* blank; *1–361,* text; *362,* blank.

Binding: Red cloth with gold lettering on spine. Rear board carries Heinemann windmill blind-stamped in lower right corner. Light brown endpapers.

Brennan 12.

18. *The Lawless Roads*

a. THE LAWLESS ROADS | *A MEXICAN JOURNEY* |

by | GRAHAM GREENE | *With Ten Illustrations* | LONGMANS, GREEN AND CO. | LONDON ◇ NEW YORK ◇ TORONTO

(218 x 138 mm.) *A* B–S⁸ T¹⁰; *1–4* 5–306 *307–308*. Black-and-white photographic plates inserted after pp. 2, 64, 104, 136, 150, 160, 186, 210.

Contents: *1*, half-title; *2*, list of books by GG; *3*, title page; *4*, copyright page: "*First published 1939*"; *5*, "Author's Note"; *6*, three quotations: from Edwin Muir, from *Wit's Recreations*, and from Cardinal Newman; *7*, table of contents; *8*, list of illustrations; 9–306, text; *307–308*, blank.

Binding: Red cloth with gold lettering on spine. Top edges stained yellow; greenish-yellow endpapers carry a map of GG's itinerary in blue ink.

Note: This copy bears the bookplate of Princesse Jean Callimachi on verso of the front free endpaper. Bertram Rota Ltd., Catalogue 162 (Autumn 1969), lists as Item 406 a copy of *LawR* in a "late binding, lettered in black and with map end-papers on white paper, not yellow."

Brennan 13.

b. THE LAWLESS | ROADS | *By* | GRAHAM GREENE | [Penguin Books seal] | PENGUIN BOOKS | HARMONDSWORTH—MIDDLESEX—ENGLAND | 245 FIFTH AVENUE NEW YORK U.S.A.

(180 x 107 mm.) Pp. *1–8* 9–256.

Contents: *1*, half-title; *2*, note from publisher; *3*, title page; *4*, copyright: "First published in Penguin Books | 1947"; *5*, Author's Note and, below, a note to the second edition by GG, citing the source of the story for *The Power and the Glory*; *6*, quotes from Edwin Muir, from *Wit's Recreations*, and from Cardinal Newman; *7*, table of contents; *8*, blank; 9–256, text.

Binding: Paperback, with pages gathered and stapled. Front cover and spine red with white banner 68 mm., centered, within which are title and author's name in black.

Rear cover, white, carries a photo and biography of GG within a red frame.

Note: Penguin Books No. 559.

19. *The Confidential Agent*

a. THE | CONFIDENTIAL AGENT | AN ENTER-TAINMENT BY | GRAHAM GREENE | [publisher's device: Heinemann windmill] | [rule] | WILLIAM HEINEMANN LTD | LONDON : : TORONTO

(190 x 126 mm.) *A* B–S⁸ T⁴; *i–viii, 1–2 3–286 287–288.*

Contents: *i–ii,* blank; *iii,* half-title; *iv,* list of books by GG; *v,* title page; *vi,* copyright page: "FIRST PUBLISHED 1939"; *vii,* table of contents; *viii,* blank; 1–286, text; *287,* publisher's solicitation of readers' opinions; *288,* blank.

Binding: Blue cloth with red lettering on spine. Rear board carries Heinemann windmill blind-stamped in lower right corner. Tan endpapers. Dust jacket: Front cover is gray with a photo of "D." on right center, over which is partially superimposed a typed confidential letter and a specimen thumbprint. At top is the title and at bottom is the author's name in black capitals. Spine is white, with gray and pink horizontal stripes. Rear cover, white, carries comments of critics on GG.

Note: See note on first American edition below (19b).

Brennan 14.

b. *THE* | CONFIDENTIAL | AGENT | *An Entertainment* | GRAHAM GREENE | [double rule, top rule bold] | NEW YORK · THE VIKING PRESS · MCMXXXIX

(189 x 124 mm.) *1–18⁸ 19⁴ 20⁸; i–viii, 1–2 3–302 303–304.*

Contents: *i–ii,* blank; *iii,* half-title; *iv,* list of books by GG; *v,* title page; *vi,* copyright page: "PUBLISHED IN SEPTEMBER 1939"; *vii,* table of contents; *viii,* blank; *1–302,* text; *303–304,* blank.

Binding: Gray cloth. Spine carries black lettering between two solid orange circles. Front board carries black outline figure of a man with two orange dots for eyes. Top edges stained yellow. Dust jacket: Front cover and spine fades from gray in the upper half to black in the lower half. Front cover carries a silhouetted man in derby and overcoat, with yellow circular light in top right and orange circular light in lower left. Title and author's name are superimposed. Rear cover, white, carries a synopsis of the novel, printed within an orange border.

Note: David Randall, in *Dukedom Large Enough* (New York: Random House, 1969), p. 236, remarks on different treatments of "certain scenes, characters, motives and ideals" between the American, English, and Dutch editions. I have not collated the texts of these copies.

Brennan 14.

c. [all within a double-rule frame, outer rule bold, divided vertically in the center by a rule; in the right half of the frame is the following:] *THE* | CONFIDENTIAL | AGENT | by | GRAHAM GREENE | *Editions for the Armed Services, Inc.* | A NON-PROFIT ORGANIZA-TION ESTABLISHED BY | THE COUNCIL ON BOOKS IN WARTIME, NEW YORK | [in the left half is the following:] PUBLISHED BY ARRANGE-MENT WITH | THE VIKING PRESS, INC., NEW YORK | [Armed Services Edition seal] | COPYRIGHT, 1939, BY GRAHAM GREENE

(100 x 138 mm.) Pp. 1 *2–4* 5–286 *287–288*.

Contents: 1, title page; *2*, note on manufacture; *3*, table of contents; *4*, blank; 5–284, text; *285–287*, brief biography of GG; *288*, Armed Services Edition seal.

Binding: Paperback, with pages gathered and stapled. Front cover blue with red border at tail and yellow label at head; superimposed is a black-and-white photo of a copy of the first American edition. Rear cover is white with a red border and white stars within the border. Inside the border printed on pale yellow is a synopsis of the novel.

Note: This title is Armed Services Edition 873. Only two of Greene's titles appeared in this series, this one and *The Ministry of Fear* (22c).

d. THE | CONFIDENTIAL | AGENT | *An Entertainment* | GRAHAM GREENE | [double rule, top rule bold] | THE SUN DIAL PRESS GARDEN CITY, N.Y.

(189 x 127 mm.) *1–8*¹⁶ *9*⁸ *10*¹⁶; *i–ii, 1–2* 3–302.

Contents: *i*, title page; *ii*, copyright page; *1*, table of contents; *2*, title for Part One; *3–302*, text.

Binding: Pale grayish-brown cloth with outline figure on front board as on first American edition but lacking orange dots for eyes and solid orange circles on spine. Top edges stained gray. Fore edges uncut. Dust jacket: Front cover is the same as on the first American edition. Spine carries a black banner at the head. Rear cover, white, advertises other titles published by the Sun Dial Press.

Note: A later printing of the first American edition (19b).

20. *The Power and the Glory*
a. THE POWER AND | THE GLORY | BY | GRAHAM GREENE | [publisher's device: Heinemann windmill] | [rule] | WILLIAM HEINEMANN LTD | LONDON :: TORONTO

(190 x 124 mm.) *A* B–S⁸; *i–vi, 1–2* 3–280 *281–282*.

Contents: *i*, half-title; *ii*, list of books by GG; *iii*, title page; *iv*, copyright page: "FIRST PUBLISHED 1940"; *v*, dedication: "FOR GERVASE"; *vi*, quote from John Dryden at top and author's disclaimer in lower right; *1–280*, text; *281–282*, blank.

Binding: Greenish-yellow cloth with purple lettering on spine. Rear board carries Heinemann windmill stamped in purple in lower right corner. Tan endpapers. Dust jacket: Front cover is purple, with title and author's name in a white label, 128 x 85 mm., in black ink framed by ornaments. Spine is purple, with title and author's name in black ink on a white label. Rear cover, white, carries critical remarks on GG quoted from reviews.

Note: According to GG, this edition was printed in only 3,500 copies (Collected Edition of *The Power and the Glory* [London: Bodley Head, 1971], p. x). This copy carries Book Society bookplate on front pastedown endpaper.

Brennan 15.

b. GRAHAM GREENE | THE | LABYRINTHINE | WAYS | [the following two lines centered within a three-sided ornamental umbrellalike frame] NEW | YORK | 1940 · THE VIKING PRESS

(203 x 134 mm.) *1–11*($\pm 11_3$) *12–16*($\pm 16_8$) *17–19*[8]; *1–9* 10–301 *302–304*.

Contents: *1*, half-title; *2*, list of books by GG; *3*, title page; *4*, copyright page: "FIRST PUBLISHED IN MARCH 1940"; *5*, dedication: "TO VIVIEN | WITH DEAREST LOVE"; *6*, blank; 7–301, text; *302–304*, blank.

Binding: Bright yellow cloth with dark blue lettering on spine. Front board carries the following at top in dark blue ink: "[in a three-sided ornamental umbrella, open on left side] G [in the same line, to the right] THE LABYRINTHINE WAYS." Rear board carries, in upper right corner, the same "G" as on front board, in ornamental umbrella open on right side. Top edges stained greenish blue. Dust jacket: Pictorial, showing on the front cover and spine in sepia, yellow, and olive a Mexican bandit behind whom is a walled maze containing a silhouetted running figure, along with a firing squad and its victim. Rear cover, white, carries a commentary on the novel.

Note: According to GG, this edition sold only 2,000 copies (Collected Edition of *The Power and the Glory* [London: Bodley Head, 1971], p. x).

Brennan 15.

21. *British Dramatists*

a. BRITISH | DRAMATISTS | [double taper rule, 60 mm.] | GRAHAM GREENE | [double taper rule, 23 mm.] | *WITH* | *8 PLATES IN COLOUR* | *AND* | *26 ILLUS-TRATIONS IN* | *BLACK & WHITE* | [ornament: classical portico] | WILLIAM COLLINS OF LONDON | MCMXXXXII

(222 x 158 mm.) *A*⁴ B⁸ C–E⁴; *1–6* 7–46 *47–48*. Color plates inserted after pp. 8, 24, 32, 40.

Contents: *1*, half-title; *2*, acknowledgment to contributors of pictures and manuscripts; *3*, title page; *4*, copyright page; *5–6*, list of illustrations; *7–48*, text.

Binding: Maroon paper. Front board carries the following in white: "[within a triple rule frame, middle rule bold] *BRITISH* | *DRAMATISTS* | [replica of an Elizabethan stage, probably the Swan] | *GRAHAM GREENE.*" Pale gray endpapers. Dust jacket: Maroon paper; front cover is a replica of the front board, as described above. Rear cover, white, carries in maroon ink a list of titles already published in the "Britain in Pictures" series.

Note: This title is one of a series titled "Britain in Pictures," edited by W. J. Turner, which, in 1942, consisted of twenty-four published titles and eighteen in preparation.

Brennan 16.

22. *The Ministry of Fear*

a. THE | MINISTRY OF FEAR | *An Entertainment* | BY | GRAHAM GREENE | [publisher's device: Heinemann windmill] | [rule] | WILLIAM HEINEMANN LTD | LONDON :: TORONTO

(184 x 120 mm.) *A* B–O⁸ P¹⁰; *i–vi*, 1–236 *237–238*.

Contents: *i*, half-title; *ii*, list of books by GG; *iii*, title page; *iv*, copyright: "FIRST PUBLISHED 1943"; *v*, table of contents; *vi*, blank; 1–236, text; *237–238*, blank.

Binding: Deep yellow cloth with black lettering on spine;

rear board carries Heinemann windmill stamped in black in lower right corner. Tan endpapers.

Note: The Lilly Library owns a copy in a pale yellow cloth binding, designated on their catalog card as "first issue" binding by an unidentified authority (Lilly PR6013. R4 M66 1943a).

Brennan 17.

b. *The MINISTRY | OF FEAR | An Entertainment by | GRAHAM GREENE |* THE VIKING PRESS • NEW YORK • 1943

(202 x 133 mm.) *1–12⁸ 13⁴ 14–16⁸; i–vi, 1–2 3–239 240– 242.*

Contents: *i*, list of books by GG; *ii*, blank; *iii*, title page; *iv*, copyright page: "PUBLISHED BY THE VIKING PRESS IN MAY 1943"; *v*, table of contents; *vi*, blank; 1–239, text; *240–242*, blank.

Binding: Black cloth. At head of the front board is the title in light blue ink. Spine carries the following: "[in light blue ink] GRAHAM GREENE | [in white] *THE MINISTRY OF FEAR* | [in light blue ink] VIKING." Top edges stained pale blue. Dust jacket: Front and spine are purple, carrying on the upper front cover a pictorial representation in white of a man staring in fear, below which is the title in yellow. Lower front cover and lower spine carry pictorial representation of a car moving down a road toward a bombed-out city. Rear cover, white, carries a synopsis of the novel in black ink.

Note: Herbert F. West's copy, with his bookplate on front pastedown endpaper. The purchase of this copy from Mr. West, in 1965 for $4.00, marked the beginning of the collection.

Brennan 17.

c. [all within a double-rule frame, divided vertically in the center by a rule; in the right half of the frame, the following:] *The MINISTRY | OF FEAR |* An Entertainment

by | Graham Greene | *Armed Services Editions* | COUN-
CIL ON BOOKS IN WARTIME, INC. | NEW YORK
| [in the left half, the following:] PUBLISHED BY
ARRANGEMENT WITH | THE VIKING PRESS,
INC., NEW YORK | Copyright, 1943, by Graham
Greene | Manufactured in the United States of America

(113 x 164 mm.) Pp. *1–2 3–255 256.*

Contents: *1*, title page; *2*, table of contents; *3–256*, text.

Binding: Paperback, with pages gathered and stapled.
Spine is blue with white lettering. Front cover is yellow
with red border at tail. Superimposed is a photo of a copy
of the first American edition. Rear cover carries brief
reviews within a red frame, printed in black ink on a
yellow background.

Note: Armed Services Edition A–22. Only two of
Greene's titles were published in this series, this one and
The Confidential Agent (19c).

d. *THE MINISTRY | OF FEAR | An Entertainment by |
Graham Greene* | THE SUN DIAL PRESS, GARDEN CITY, N.Y.

(198 x 137 mm.) *1–6*^{16} *7*^{12} *8*^{16}; *i–vi, 1–2 3–239 240–242.*

Contents: *i*, list of books by GG; *ii*, blank; *iii*, title page;
iv, copyright page; *v*, table of contents; *vi*, blank; *1–239*,
text; *240–242*, blank.

Binding: Gray stippled paper with blue lettering on spine.
Front board carries title at the head in blue ink. Top edges
stained blue; pale brownish-white endpapers. Fore edges
uncut. Dust jacket: Front cover carries a collage of stills
from the film of *MF*, which continues on the spine and
rear cover. Superimposed on front is the title in white on
a light blue banner.

Note: A printing of the first American edition, described
above (22b).

23. *The Little Train*
  a. THE LITTLE TRAIN | [in red] DOROTHY CRAIGIE
   | [illustration of a steam locomotive]

(176 x 243 mm.) *1–3*⁸; *i–iii*, 1–42 *43–45*.

Contents: *i*, title page; *ii*, dedication: "To the guard of the twelve o'clock to Brighton." and colophon: "This book is printed for EYRE AND SPOTTISWOODE | (Publishers) Ltd., 14, 15 & 16 Bedford Street, | London, W.C.2, by Jarrold and Sons, Ltd., | The Empire Press, Norwich"; *iii*, a picture of The Little Train; *1–44*, text: *45*, three vertical puffs of smoke.

Binding: Yellow cloth. Front board is decorated with steam locomotives in red, black, and green, with title and author's name at head. Rear board carries a black lantern, centered, with red light. Endpapers are decorated with a map. Dust jacket: Light blue with wispy white mottling, decorated in the same manner as front and rear boards.

Note: GG acknowledged authorship of this title on the title page of *The Little Fire Engine* (see 27a).

Brennan 18.

24. *Nineteen Stories*

a. NINETEEN STORIES | BY | GRAHAM GREENE | [publisher's device: Heinemann windmill] | [rule] | WILLIAM HEINEMANN LTD | LONDON : : TORONTO

(184 x 122 mm.) *A* B–G¹⁶ H⁸; *i–viii*, 1–231 *232*.

Contents: *i–ii*, blank; *iii*, half-title; *iv*, list of books by GG; *v*, title page; *vi*, copyright: "FIRST PUBLISHED 1947"; *vii*, table of contents; *viii*, author's note on the stories; 1–231, text; *232*, blank.

Binding: Dark blue cloth with silver lettering on spine. Rear board carries Heinemann windmill blind-stamped in lower right corner. Tan endpapers. Dust jacket: White; front cover carries title and author's name in red and gray ink within a single-rule gray frame. Rear cover carries a list of forthcoming fiction titles in red ink.

Brennan 19.

25. *The Heart of the Matter*

a. THE HEART | OF THE MATTER | BY | GRAHAM
GREENE | [publisher's device: Heinemann windmill]
| [rule] | WILLIAM HEINEMANN LTD | MEL-
BOURNE : : LONDON : : TORONTO

(185 x 120 mm.) *A* B–I¹⁶ K⁸; *i–vi*, 1–297 *298*.

Contents: *i*, half-title; *ii*, list of books by GG; *iii*, title
page; *iv*, copyright: "FIRST PUBLISHED 1948"; *v*, dedi-
cation, "TO V.G., | L.C.G., | *and* F.C.G." and author's
note and disclaimer; *vi*, quote from Péguy; 1–297, text;
298, blank.

Binding: Dark blue cloth with silver lettering on spine.
Rear board carries Heinemann windmill blind-stamped in
lower right corner. Top edges stained orange; tan endpapers. Dust jacket: Front cover and spine are red with
white lettering. Rear cover, white, advertises the Uniform
Edition of GG's works, in a single-rule red frame.
Wrapped around the dust jacket is a separate green paper
banner with "*Book Society Choice*" in white on the front,
spine, and rear of the banner.

Note: Book Society copies of this edition carry the following statement on copyright page, p. *iv:* "THIS EDI-
TION ISSUED ON FIRST PUBLICATION BY | THE
BOOK SOCIETY, LTD., IN ASSOCIATION WITH
| WILLIAM HEINEMANN LTD | MAY 1948."

Brennan 20.

b. Presentation copy of the first English edition, identical to
25a but lacking the Book Society Choice paper banner.
Signed on recto of front free endpaper, as follows: "[in
pencil] Herbert Greene | [in blue ink, in another hand]
Audrey from Graham Greene | (A. B. Greene | Bale Cot-
tage | Plumpton | Sussex) | [signed in blue ink by GG]
Graham Greene."

c. GRAHAM GREENE | The | Heart | of the | Matter |
New York • The Viking Press • 1948

(204 x 133 mm.) 1^{16} (1_1+1) 2–10^{16}; *i–xiv, 1–2 3–306 307–308.*

Contents: *i–ii*, blank; *iii*, "THIS COPY OF | THE HEART OF THE MATTER | IS ONE OF 750 COPIES OF | THE FIRST EDITION SPECIALLY | BOUND FOR DISTRIBUTION TO | FRIENDS OF THE VIKING PRESS"; *iv*, blank; *v*, half-title; *vi*, list of books by GG; *vii*, title page; *viii*, copyright: "PUBLISHED BY THE VIKING PRESS | IN JULY 1948"; *ix*, dedication: "TO | V.G., | L.C.G., | AND | F.C.G."; *x*, blank; *xi*, quote from Péguy; *xii*, blank; *xiii*, author's note and disclaimer; *xiv*, blank; *1–306*, text; *307–308*, blank.

Binding: Gray cloth. Front board carries red and gold design and interlocking initials GG. Top edges stained red. Glassine dust jacket, as issued.

d. GRAHAM GREENE | The | Heart | of the | Matter | New York • The Viking Press • 1948

(203 x 135 mm.) 1–10^{16}; *i–xii, 1–2 3–306 307–308.*

Contents: *i–ii*, blank; *iii*, half-title; *iv*, list of books by GG; *v*, title page; *vi*, copyright: "PUBLISHED BY THE VIKING PRESS | IN JULY 1948"; *vii*, dedication: "TO | V.G., | L.C.G., | AND | F.C.G."; *viii*, blank; *ix*, quote from Péguy; *x*, blank; *xi*, author's note and disclaimer; *xii*, blank; *1–306*, text; *307–308*, blank.

Binding: Dark purple paper boards with embossed linen graining; purple lettering on quarter gray cloth spine. Front board carries interlocking initials GG in gray, interlocked between horizontal lines extending 5 cm. from the gray cloth of spine. Top edges stained dark purple. Dust jacket: Front cover is divided diagonally into two halves, the left being grayish-green and the right, dark purple, with title and author's name in white capital letters. The spine is grayish-green with white lettering. Rear cover, white with grayish-green banner at head, carries "advance comments" on the novel.

Note: A printing of the same edition as 25c. The first trade printing.

Brennan 20.

26. *The Third Man*

a. [first two lines in upper left] GRAHAM | GREENE | [silhouette of man with left hand raised, cat pawing at his left leg] | THE | THIRD MAN | NEW YORK · THE VIKING PRESS · 1950

(186 x 124 mm.) $1-5^{16}$; *1–6* 7–157 *158–160*.

Contents: *1*, half-title; *2*, list of books by GG; *3*, title page; *4*, copyright: "PUBLISHED BY THE VIKING PRESS IN MARCH 1950"; *5*, dedication to Carol Reed; *6*, blank; 7–10, Preface, dated February 1950; *11*, half-title; *12*, blank; 13–157, text; *158–160*, blank.

Binding: Gray cloth paper boards with black lettering on orange cloth spine. Top edges stained gray. Dust jacket: Front cover and spine are orange with white and black lettering. Rear cover, white, carries comments on the film.

Brennan 22.

b. THE 3rd | MAN | [silhouette, man with left arm raised, between two diagonal lines] | by | GRAHAM | GREENE | [Bantam seal] | BANTAM BOOKS   NEW YORK

(162 x 108 mm.) Pp. *i–iv, 1* 2–118 *119–124*.

Contents: *i*, brief plot synopsis; *ii*, brief note on film; *iii*, title page; *iv*, copyright: "Bantam Edition Published April, 1950, | *1st Printing . . . March 1950*"; 1–118, text; *119–124*, advertisement of Bantam titles.

Binding: Paperback, perfect binding, with yellow spine. Front cover carries black-and-white still of Joseph Cotten and Valli, behind whom is blue-green background and brown silhouette of a man. Author's name and title at head. Rear cover is white, with comment on GG.

c. THE THIRD MAN | *and* | THE FALLEN IDOL | *by* | GRAHAM GREENE | [publisher's device: Heinemann windmill] | [rule] | WILLIAM HEINEMANN LTD | MELBOURNE : : LONDON : : TORONTO

(182 x 121 mm.) A B–L^8 M^{10}; *i–vi, 1–2* 3–188 *189–190*.

Contents: *i*, half-title; *ii*, list of books by GG; *iii*, title page; *iv*, copyright: "FIRST PUBLISHED 1950"; *v*, dedication to Carol Reed; *vi*, blank; *1*, half-title: "THE THIRD MAN"; *2*, blank; 3–6, Preface; 7–142, text; *143*, half-title: "THE FALLEN IDOL"; *144*, blank; 145–146, Preface; 147–188, text; *189–190*, blank.

Binding: Black cloth with silver lettering on spine. Rear board carries Heinemann windmill blind-stamped in lower right corner. Tan endpapers. Dust jacket: Black-and-white stills. Front cover shows a scene from *The Third Man;* superimposed are titles and author's name in red letters outlined in white. Rear cover carries scene from *The Fallen Idol.*

Brennan 22.

d. [in upper right] MODERN | FILM | SCRIPTS | [in lower right] THE THIRD MAN | a film by | Graham Greene | and Carol Reed | Lorrimer, London

(202 x 138 mm.) *1*^{8} 2^{12} *3*^{8} 4^{12} *5*^{8} 6^{12} 7^8; *1–4* 5–134 *135–136*.

Contents: *1*, title page; 2, copyright: "First printing 1969"; *3*, table of contents; *4*, acknowledgments: "We wish to thank Carol Reed, who was kind enough to lend his personal copy of the script, and Graham Greene, who personally vetted it before publication"; 5–6, Introduction; 7–9, list of main characters; 10, credits list; 11, cast list; 12–13, note on the transition from shooting script to film; *14*, blank; 15–134, text; *135*, blank; *136*, blank, with printed insert pasted in: "The film *The Third Man* is owned and distributed by British Lion Films Ltd."

Binding: Stiff paper wrappers, with black lettering on white spine. Front cover carries still from the film of Orson Welles; in lower right are title, author's name, and director's name in white letters. Upper half of rear cover carries a still of Joseph Cotten and Trevor Howard; bottom half is olive in color, with a list of titles in the film series.

Lorrimer Series no. 13.

27. *The Little Fire Engine*

    a. [the following in dark blue ink, with title in italic script, in an arc at head of title page] *The Little Fire Engine* | BY THE AUTHOR OF THE LITTLE TRAIN | GRAHAM GREENE | *ILLUSTRATED BY* | DOROTHY CRAIGIE | [lower half of page is decorated with yellow fire helmets and blue axes]

    (177 x 280 mm.) *1–3*⁸; *i–ii*, 1–44 *45–46*.

    Contents: *i*, title page; *ii*, colophon: "This book is printed for MAX PARRISH & CO. LTD | Adprint House, Rathbone Place, London W1 | by Jarrold and Sons Ltd, | The Empire Press, Norwich"; 1–44, text; *45*, illustration of firehouse; *46*, blank.

    Binding: Pictorial paper, decorated by Craigie. Front board is red, with illustration of a fireman. Title is in white, and author's and illustrator's names are in black. Rear board is dark blue with illustration of fire wagon. Text in dark blue ink. Top edges stained red; decorated endpapers. Dust jacket: Identical to pictorial binding.

    Note: A proof copy in the Lilly Library indicates that Greene had initially intended to allow Dorothy Craigie to take credit for this title, as he had done for *The Little Train*. Its title page lists Craigie as the author (Lilly PZ7.G75L74 1950). See 23a.

    Brennan 23.

28. *The Lost Childhood and Other Essays*

    a. THE | LOST CHILDHOOD | and other essays | by | GRAHAM GREENE | 1951 | EYRE & SPOTTISWOODE | London

    (216 x 136 mm.) *A* B–M⁸; *i–iv* v *vi* vii–viii *ix–xii*, 13–191 *192*.

Contents: *i*, half-title; *ii*, list of books by GG; *iii* title page; *iv*, printer's imprint; v, acknowledgments; *vi*, blank; vii–viii, table of contents; *ix*, half-title; *x*, blank; *xi*–191, text; *192*, blank.

Binding: Tan cloth with gold lettering on spine. Top edges stained red. Dust jacket: Front cover and spine are red with decorations. Front cover carries the dust-jacket credit "STEIN" in lower right corner. Rear cover, white, carries a photo of GG and a brief profile.

Brennan 24.

b. The American publication, identical to the English, with the following exceptions:

Title page: THE | LOST CHILDHOOD | and other essays | by | GRAHAM GREENE | 1952 | THE VIKING PRESS | New York

Contents: p. *iv* carries only two statements, "[at head] COPYRIGHT 1951 BY GRAHAM GREENE | [at tail] *Printed in Great Britain.*"

Binding: Brown cloth with gold lettering on spine. Top edges stained yellow. Dust jacket: Identical to that of the English edition, except that the front cover is not signed "STEIN." At tail of spine is "Viking." Rear cover carries excerpts from reviews.

Note: The American publication consists of sheets of the English edition in a different binding, with variant title and copyright pages.

Brennan 24.

29. *The End of the Affair*

a. THE END OF THE | AFFAIR | *by* | GRAHAM GREENE | [publisher's device: Heinemann windmill] | [rule] | WILLIAM HEINEMANN LTD | MELBOURNE : : LONDON : : TORONTO

(182 x 120 mm.) *A* B–O^8 P^{10}; *i–vi*, 1–237 *238*.

Contents: *i*, half-title; *ii*, list of books by GG; *iii*, title page; *iv*, copyright: "FIRST PUBLISHED 1951"; *v*, dedication: "To C."; *vi*, quote from Léon Bloy; 1–237, text; *238*, blank.

Binding: Gray cloth with gold lettering on spine. Rear board carries Heinemann windmill blind-stamped in lower right corner. Tan endpapers. Dust jacket: Front cover and spine are gray with white lettering in the upper half and white with gray lettering in the lower half. Rear cover, white, carries a list of the titles published in GG's Uniform Edition series.

Brennan 25.

b. *Graham Green* | [the title within a single-rule label decorated on each vertical side with a vertical row of ornaments and a vertical rule] THE | *End of the Affair* | *New York* | THE VIKING PRESS | MCMLI

(202 x 134 mm.) 1–3^{16} 4–5^{14} 6–8^{16}; *i–vi*, 1–2 3–240 *241–242*.

Contents: *i*, half-title; *ii*, list of books by GG; *iii*, title page; *iv*, copyright: "PUBLISHED BY THE VIKING PRESS IN OCTOBER 1951"; *v*, dedication: "TO CATHERINE | *with love*"; *vi*, blank; *1*, half-title and quote from Léon Bloy; *2*, blank; 3–240, text; *241–242*, blank.

Binding: Light brown cloth front board with black cloth rear board and spine. Gold lettering and green ink decoration on spine. Front board carries title in green ink, within an ornamental frame identical to that of title page. Top edges stained green. Dust jacket: Front cover and spine are green with scalloped gold borders at the head and tail. Superimposed are the title in white and the author's name in gold letters. Rear cover, white, carries a quote from Evelyn Waugh on GG within a gold ornamental frame.

Note: Variant binding: Tan cloth. Front board carries title in brown ink, within a brown ornamental frame. Green lettering and brown decoration on spine. Top edges stained green. Copy lacks dust jacket but is identical in all other respects to 29b (E. R. Hagemann copy).

Brennan 25.

30. *The Living Room*

a. THE LIVING ROOM | *A Play in Two Acts* | BY | GRAHAM GREENE | [small black five-pointed star] | [publisher's device: Heinemann windmill] | [rule] | WILLIAM HEINEMANN LTD | MELBOURNE : : LONDON : : TORONTO

(182 x 120 mm.) *A* B–E^8; *i–x*, 1–67 *68–70*.

Contents: *i–ii*, blank; *iii*, half-title; *iv*, list of books by GG; *v*, title page; *vi*, copyright: "FIRST PUBLISHED 1953"; *vii*, dedication: "To | CATHERINE WITH LOVE"; *viii*, list of characters; *ix*, list of scenes; *x*, note on original performance; 1–67, text; *68–70*, blank.

Binding: Red cloth with gold lettering on spine. Rear board carries Heinemann windmill blind-stamped in lower right corner. Dust jacket: Front cover carries a black-and-white still from the performance, showing Dorothy Tutin and Eric Portman. At head is the author's name in red; at tail is the title in white. Spine and rear cover are white with red and black lettering on the spine. Rear cover carries a list of GG's titles in the Uniform Edition series.

Note: *LR* was first published in Sweden, translated from manuscript, under the title *I Sista Rummet* (Stockholm: Norstedt, 1952).

Brennan 28.

b. Association copy of first English edition, the second impression, presented by Eric Portman, the star of the original cast, to Jessica Altman, dated "Wyndham's Theatre 1953." Presentation inscription on p. *i*. On p. *vi* is the additional note, "REPRINTED 1953." On inside front flap of dust jacket is additional note, "2nd impression." Otherwise physically identical to the first impression (30a).

c. THE | Living Room | A PLAY IN TWO ACTS BY | Graham Greene | New York • THE VIKING PRESS • 1954

(187 x 120 mm.) *1–4*^{16}; *1–10* 11–126 *127–128*.

Contents: *1*, half-title; *2*, list of books by GG; *3*, title page; *4*, copyright: "Published by The Viking Press in May 1954"; *5*, dedication: "To Catherine | with love"; *6*, blank; 7, note on first performance; *8*, list of scenes; *9*, fly-title; *10*, blank; 11–126, text; *127–128*, blank.

Binding: Purple decorated paper boards with red lettering on gray cloth spine. Dust jacket: Front cover and spine are purple with white lettering. Rear cover, white, carries quotes from reviews printed in purple.

Brennan 28.

31. *The Little Horse Bus*

   a. [title page covers verso and recto pages] *The Little Horse Bus* | GRAHAM GREENE | *ILLUSTRATED BY* | DOROTHY CRAIGIE | [two-page illustration of Horse Bus pursuing thieves in a hansom] | COPYRIGHT 1952 · PRINTED IN GREAT BRITAIN BY JARROLD & SONS LIMITED NORWICH MAX PARRISH · LONDON

   (215 x 180 mm.) I^1 2–5^4 6^1; *1–3* 4–35 *36* [pp. *1–2* and *35–36* constitute front and rear free endpapers].

   Contents: *1*, color illustration, continuing onto pastedown endpaper; *2–3*, title page and copyright; 4–35, text; *36*, color illustration, continuing onto pastedown endpaper.

   Binding: Red cloth with gold lettering on spine. Front board carries Horse Bus, stamped in gold. Top edges stained red. Dust jacket: Illustrated in red, yellow, gray, and blue. Front cover carries a Horse Bus in the lower half and the title, author's name, and illustrator's name in a gray label. The spine is yellow with red and blue lettering. Rear cover is blue with white stars.

   Brennan 29.

32. *Essais Catholiques*

   a. *GRAHAM GREENE* | ESSAIS CATHOLIQUES | TRADUCTION DÉ | MARCELLE SIBON | *ÉDITIONS DU SEUIL* | 27, *rue Jacob, Paris VI*ᵉ

(188 x 133 mm.) *1* 2–8⁸; *1–8* 9–120 *121–128*.

Contents: *1–2*, blank; *3*, half-title; *4*, list of works by GG; *5*, title page; *6*, blank; 7–*121*, text; *122*, blank; *123–125*, table of contents; *126*, colophon: "ACHEVÉ D' IM-PRIMER | SUR ALFA CELLUNAF | EN 1953 PAR | ANDRE TOURNON ET Cⁱᵉ | D.L. 1ᵉʳ tr. 1953 – n° | 533 | (n° 630)"; *127–128*, blank.

Binding: Paper wrappers with photograph of bas relief figure of a saint, in gray tones, on front and rear cover. Front cover carries the following: "[in green] *Graham Greene* | [in black] ESSAIS CATHOLIQUES | [in green] *Traduit de l'anglais par* | MARCELLE SIBON | *Éditions du Seuil*." Spine, gray, carries author's name and name of series in green, title in black.

Brennan 27.

33. *The Little Steamroller*

a. [title page covers verso and recto pages; p. 2, pictorial illustration of a thief wheeling away a baggage cart; in lower left corner in a white signboard, in brown ink:] FIRST PUBLISHED 1955 · PRINTED IN GREAT BRITAIN | BY GRAPHICS REPRODUCTIONS LTD LONDON | [p. 3, pictorial illustration, with title in red in upper half in a gray signboard] *The Little Steamroller* | [in green] A STORY OF ADVENTURE, MYSTERY AND DETECTION | GRAHAM GREENE | Illus-trated By DOROTHY CRAIGIE | [illustration of Bill Driver and the Little Steamroller] | [at tail, in a white signboard, in brown ink] LOTHROP, LEE & SHEPARD CO., INC. | 419 FOURTH AVENUE, NEW YORK 16, N.Y.

(212 x 182 mm.) *1–3*⁶; *1–7* 8–33 *34–36*.

Contents: *1*, half-title; *2–3*, title page; *4–36*, text.

Binding: Yellow cloth-grained paper boards with black lettering on spine. Front cover carries the title and a pic-torial representation of a steamroller stamped in black.

Brennan 30.

34. *Loser Takes All*

a. LOSER TAKES ALL | *by* | GRAHAM GREENE | [publisher's device: Heinemann windmill] | [rule] | WILLIAM HEINEMANN LTD | MELBOURNE : : LONDON : : TORONTO

(183 x 122 mm.) *A* B–H^8 I^{10}; *i–viii*, *1–2* 3–140.

Contents: *i–ii*, blank; *iii*, half-title; *iv*, list of books by GG; *v*, title page; *vi*, copyright: "FIRST PUBLISHED 1955"; *vii*, letter from GG to Frere; *viii*, blank; *1–140*, text.

Binding: Dark blue cloth with gold lettering on spine. Front board carries title in frame at head, in gold. Rear board carries Heinemann windmill blind-stamped in lower right corner. Dust jacket: Yellow, blue, and white pictorial front cover; the spine is yellow with blue lettering. Rear cover, white, advertises *The End of the Affair* in single-rule frame.

Brennan 32.

b. Proof copy, identical to first English edition.

Binding: Pale bluish-green paper wrappers with black lettering on spine. Front cover carries the following: *"PROOF COPY* | [ripple rule] | LOSER TAKES ALL | *Graham Greene* | [ripple rule]."

35. *The Quiet American*

a. THE | QUIET AMERICAN | *by* | GRAHAM GREENE | [publisher's device: Heinemann windmill] | [rule] | WILLIAM HEINEMANN LTD | MELBOURNE : : LONDON : : TORONTO

(196 x 128 mm.) *A* B–H^{16}; *i–viii*, *1–2* 3–247 *248*.

Contents: *i*, half-title; *ii*, list of books by GG; *iii*, title page; *iv*, copyright: "FIRST PUBLISHED 1955"; *v*, dedicatory letter to "Réné and Phuong"; *vi*, blank; *vii*, quotes from Arthur Hugh Clough and Lord Byron; *viii*, blank; *1–247*, text, with date *"March 1952–June 1955"* on p. 247; *248*, blank.

Binding: Dark blue cloth with gold lettering on spine. Rear board carries Heinemann windmill blind-stamped in lower right corner. Top edges stained blue. Dust jacket: Front cover and spine are white with gray design; author's name is in red in upper half of the front cover and title is in black in lower half. Rear cover, white, carries quotes from reviews of *Loser Takes All*.

Note: *QA* was first published in Sweden, translated from manuscript, as *Den Stillsame Amerikanen* (Stockholm: Norstedt, 1955).

Brennan 33.

b. Proof copy, identical to the first English edition, in white paper wrappers with the following on front cover: "[all the following in red] *PROOF COPY* | [ripple rule] | THE QUIET AMERICAN | *Graham Greene* | [ripple rule]." Red lettering on spine.

c. *GRAHAM GREENE* | [ornamental rule] | *The Quiet American* | NEW YORK · THE VIKING PRESS · 1956 (203 x 133 mm.) *1–8¹⁶; i–vi, 1–2 3–249 250.*

Contents: *i*, half-title; *ii*, list of books by GG; *iii*, title page; *iv*, copyright: "PUBLISHED BY THE VIKING PRESS IN MARCH 1956"; *v*, dedicatory letter to Réné and Phuong; *vi*, quotes from A. H. Clough and Lord Byron; *1–249*, text, with the date *"March 1952–June 1955"* on p. 249; *250*, blank.

Binding: Brown paper boards with imitation leather design; gold lettering on quarter black cloth spine. Top edges stained brown. Dust jacket: Front cover and spine are decorated in red and black, with the title and author's name in black within gold labels on the front cover and spine. Rear cover, white, carries excerpts from English reviews of *The Quiet American*.

Brennan 33.

d. THE | QUIET AMERICAN | *by* | GRAHAM GREENE | [publisher's device: Heinemann windmill] |

WILLIAM HEINEMANN / NEDERLAND | THE HAGUE

(181 x 112 mm.) *1–7¹⁶ 8⁸; 1–6 7–239 240.*

Contents: *1*, half-title; *2*, list of books by GG; *3*, title page; *4*, copyright: "First Continental edition | Oct. 1957"; *5*, dedicatory letter to Réné and Phuong; *6*, quotes from Arthur Hugh Clough and Lord Byron; *7–239*, text, with the date *"March 1952–June 1955"* on p. 239; *240*, blank.

Binding: Red cloth with gold lettering on spine. Dust jacket: Identical to that of first English edition, except that the rear cover is blank.

Note: This "continental" publication constitutes a new edition.

e. Another copy of the "First Continental edition," identical to 35d, above, but bound in paper wrappers. Decorations on wrappers identical to those of dust jacket of 35d.

36. *The Potting Shed*

a. THE | POTTING SHED | *A Play in Three Acts* | *by* | GRAHAM GREENE | [publisher's device: Heinemann windmill] | [rule] | WILLIAM HEINEMANN LTD | MELBOURNE : : LONDON : : TORONTO

(182 x 121 mm.) *A* B–D⁸ E⁴ F⁸; *i–viii, 1–79 80.*

Contents: *i*, half-title; *ii*, list of books by GG; *iii*, title page; *iv*, copyright page varies considerably from first English edition, below; it carries the date, "FIRST PUBLISHED 1957"; *v*, list of characters; *vi*, note on first American performance with date of performance indicated by ellipses and lacking GG's note on text; *vii*, list of scenes; *viii*, blank; *1–79*, text; *80*, blank.

Binding: Tan paper wrappers with black lettering on spine. Front cover carries the following: *"UNCORRECTED PROOF COPY* | (NOT FOR SALE) | [ripple rule] | THE POTTING SHED | *Graham Greene* | [ripple rule]." Rear cover is defaced with numerical computations in handwriting.

Note: The text of this copy follows that of the American edition, which GG changed for the first English edition published in 1958 (see p. *vi* of that edition). This copy establishes the fact that the play was in press in both countries with the same text before the decision was made to return to the original version. See R. H. Miller, "Graham Greene, *The Potting Shed*, Act III," *PBSA*, 71 (1977), 105–7.

b. [ornamental rule] | The | Potting Shed | A PLAY IN THREE ACTS BY | Graham Greene | New York • THE VIKING PRESS • 1957

(203 x 133 mm.) *1–4*¹⁶; *1–6* 7 *8* 9 *10–12* 13–123 *124–128*. Black-and-white photo plate inserted after p. *4*.

Contents: *1*, half-title; *2*, blank; *3*, list of books by GG; *4*, blank; *5*, title page; *6*, copyright: "FIRST PUBLISHED IN 1957 BY THE VIKING PRESS"; 7, note on first performance; *8*, blank; 9, list of scenes; *10*, blank; *11*–123, text; *124–128*, blank.

Binding: Tan cloth with green lettering on spine. Front board carries title and author's name in green between two green ornamental rules. Dust jacket: Tan paper. Front cover carries the author's name, title, and illustration in green of a girl peering in a door. Green lettering on spine. Rear cover carries critical comments on *The Potting Shed* in green.

Brennan 34.

c. Another copy, lacking dust jacket, identical to the first American edition described above, with these exceptions:

Title page lacks date.

(207 x 133 mm.) Perfect bound; *1–6* 7 *8* 9 *10–12* 13–34 [2] 35–51 *52–54* 55–80 [2] 81–95 *96–98* 99–123 *124–130*. Black-and-white photos also appear before pp. *5*, 35, 67, *97*.

Contents: *1–2*, front free endpaper; *3*, half-title; *4*, photo; *5*, title page; *6*, copyright, with additional note: "PHOTO-

GRAPHS COURTESY OF BURT OWEN"; 7, note on first performance; *8*, blank; 9, list of scenes; *10*, blank; *11*, half-title to Act I; *12*, blank; 13–34, text of Act I, Scene i; [2], recto is half-title to Act I, Scene ii, verso blank; 35–51, text; *52*, blank; *53*, half-title to Act II; *54*, blank; 55–80, text; [2], recto is half-title for Act II, Scene ii, verso blank; 81–95, text; *96*, blank; *97*, half-title for Act III; *98*, blank; 99–123, text; *124–128*, blank; *129–130*, rear free endpaper.

Binding: Pale greenish-yellow cloth.

d. THE | POTTING SHED | *A Play in Three Acts* | *by* | GRAHAM GREENE | [publisher's device: Heinemann windmill] | HEINEMANN | LONDON MELBOURNE TORONTO

(183 x 120 mm.) *A* B–D⁸ E¹⁰; *i–viii*, 1–76.

Contents: *i*, half-title; *ii*, list of books by GG; *iii*, title page; *iv*, copyright: "First published 1958"; *v*, list of characters; *vi*, note on first performance and author's note on the text; *vii*, list of scenes; *viii*, blank; 1–76, text.

Binding: Blue cloth with gold lettering on spine. Rear board carries Heinemann windmill blind-stamped in lower right corner. Dust jacket: Dark green front cover and spine with title in orange and author's name in white, on front cover. Rear cover, white, carries a list of GG's books in green ink.

Brennan 34.

e. THE POTTING SHED | A Play in Three Acts | by | GRAHAM GREENE | [ornament, 25 x 25 mm.: masks of Comedy and Tragedy over an opened book] | LONDON | SAMUEL FRENCH LIMITED [n.d.]

(215 x 138 mm.) *A* B–C⁸ D¹⁰; *i–iv*, 1–64. Photographic plates inserted after pp. *iv*, 24, 38.

Contents: *i*, title page; *ii*, copyright; *iii*, note on first performance and synopsis of scenes; *iv*, note on royalties; 1–58, text; 59–62, furniture and property list; 63, lighting plot; 64, effects plot.

Binding: Light blue paper wrappers with black lettering on spine. Front cover: *"French's Acting Edition* 6s net | [in red] THE POTTING SHED | [in black] A Play | [in red] GRAHAM GREENE | [in black] SAMUEL FRENCH LIMITED."

37. *Our Man in Havana*

a. GRAHAM GREENE | [double rule, upper rule bold] | Our Man in Havana | AN ENTERTAINMENT | [publisher's device: Heinemann windmill] | HEINEMANN | LONDON MELBOURNE TORONTO

   (195 x 126 mm.) *A* B–H^{16} I^{12}; *i–vi, 1–2 3–273 274.*

   Contents: *i,* half-title; *ii,* list of books by GG; *iii,* title page; *iv,* copyright: "First published 1958"; *v,* disclaimer note; *vi,* quote from George Herbert; *1–273,* text; *274,* blank.

   Binding: Blue cloth boards with gold lettering on spine. Rear board carries Heinemann windmill blind-stamped in lower right corner. Dust jacket: Front cover and spine carry a pictorial decoration of the facade of a house with overhanging foliage, in purple, dark blue, and green. Superimposed are author's name in white and title in yellow. Rear cover, white, carries critical excerpts on *The Quiet American,* in dark blue.

   Brennan 35.

b. [double rule, lower rule rippled] | GRAHAM GREENE | *Our Man* | *in Havana* | AN ENTERTAINMENT | *"And the sad man is cock of all his jests."* | —GEORGE HERBERT | *1958* | THE VIKING PRESS · NEW YORK | [double rule, upper rule rippled]

   (210 x 134 mm.) *1–8^{16}; i–vi, 1–2 3–247 248–250.*

   Contents: *i,* half-title; *ii,* list of books by GG; *iii,* title page; *iv,* copyright page; *v,* author's disclaimer note; *vi,* blank; *1–247,* text; *248–250,* blank.

   Binding: Pink cloth with black lettering on spine. Front board carries figure of vacuum sweeper salesman in lower

right corner, stamped in black. Top edges stained yellow.
Dust jacket: Spine and left half of front cover are dark
brownish-black blending into pinkish-orange on right half
of front cover. Vacuum sweeper salesman stands in upper
right corner. Superimposed on lower half of front cover is
a mechanical diagram on a sheet of paper, with title in
yellow and author's name in white in upper half of the
front cover. Spine has yellow and white lettering. Rear
cover, white, carries two excerpts from the novel.

Brennan 35.

c. OUR MAN | IN HAVANA | An Entertainment | *by* |
GRAHAM GREENE | [Reprint Society seal] | THE
REPRINT SOCIETY LTD: LONDON

(185 x 120 mm.) *1* 2–7¹⁶; *1–7* 8–223 *224*.

Contents: *1*, half-title; *2*, list of books by GG; *3*, title
page; *4*, copyright: "THIS EDITION PUBLISHED BY
THE REPRINT SOCIETY LTD | BY ARRANGE-
MENT WITH WILLIAM HEINEMANN LTD 1960";
5, author's disclaimer note; *6*, quote from George Herbert; 7–223, text; *224*, blank.

Binding: Cream-colored paper boards with dark green
paper spine. Spine carries at head a deep brown label with
gold lettering; tail of spine carries Reprint Society seal in
gold. Top edges stained red. Dust jacket: Front cover
and spine carry a pictorial street scene in green, black,
and pink, with white lettering. Rear cover carries a list
of forthcoming books, within a green triple-rule frame,
outer rule bold.

38. *The Complaisant Lover*

a. THE | COMPLAISANT | LOVER | *A Comedy* | GRA-
HAM GREENE | [publisher's device: Heinemann wind-
mill] | HEINEMANN | LONDON MELBOURNE
TORONTO

(185 x 121 mm.) *A* B–D⁸ E⁴ F⁸; *i–x*, 1–77 *78*.

Contents: *i–ii*, blank; *iii*, half-title; *iv*, list of books by GG;
v, title page; *vi*, copyright: "First published 1959"; *vii*,

list of characters; *viii*, note on first performance; *ix*, synopsis of scenes; *x*, blank; 1–77, text; 77, "*Postscript on Censorship*": note on the Lord Chamberlain's objection to certain lines in the play; *78*, blank.

Binding: Dark blue cloth with gold lettering on spine. Rear board carries Heinemann windmill blind-stamped in lower right corner. Cream-colored endpapers. Dust jacket: Pale bluish-green, with author's name and title in dark blue and red on front cover and spine. Rear cover carries a list of other Heinemann plays.

Brennan 36.

b. THE | COMPLAISANT | LOVER | *A Comedy* | GRA-HAM GREENE | [publisher's device: Viking ship] | NEW YORK: THE VIKING PRESS

(203 x 132 mm.) *1–6*^{8}; *i–vi, 1–2 3–87 88–90.*

Contents: *i*, half-title; *ii*, list of books by GG; *iii*, title page; *iv*, copyright: "Published in 1961 by The Viking Press, Inc."; *v*, note on first performance; *vi*, blank; *1*, half-title; *2*, list of characters and scenes; 3–87, text; *88–90*, blank.

Binding: Decorated red paper boards with red lettering on cream-colored cloth spine. Dust jacket: Front cover and spine red with lettering in white. Front cover carries three faces in white arranged diagonally between title (above) and author's name (below). Rear cover is white, with advertisements of other Viking drama publications in red.

Brennan 36.

c. Another copy, a new printing, in the Fireside Theatre Book Club series, identical to the first American edition (37b), with the following exceptions:

(208 x 133 mm.)

Contents: *ii*, blank; *iv*, lacks LC card number.

Binding: Pale blue stippled paper boards with black lettering on gray cloth spine. Fore edges uncut. Dust jacket: Pale blue. Front cover carries in the upper half a black-

and-white photo of the three principal actors in the play; in the middle, title is in white and in the lower third, author's name is in white. Spine has white lettering. On inner front flap at tail is the notation "FIRESIDE THE-ATRE | BOOK CLUB | EDITION."

d. THE | COMPLAISANT LOVER | A Play In Two Acts | by | GRAHAM GREENE | SAMUEL [ornament, 25 mm. square: masks of Comedy and Tragedy above an opened book] FRENCH | LONDON

(215 x 137 mm.) A B–E^8; i–iv, 1 2–74 75–76. Photographic plates after pp. 2, 26.

Contents: i, title page; ii, copyright; iii, note on first performance and synopsis of scenes; iv, note on performance rights; 1–67, text; 68–72, furniture and property list; 73–74, lighting plot; 75, effects plot; 76, blank.

Binding: Medium blue wrappers with red lettering on spine. Front cover carries the following "[handwritten in ink in upper right] Bill Hunt | [all the following in red] THE | COMPLAISANT | LOVER | A Play | GRAHAM GREENE | FRENCH'S ACTING EDITION."

39. *A Visit to Morin*

a. [all the following within a green triple-rule frame, second rule bold] GRAHAM GREENE | A Visit to Morin | HEINEMANN | LONDON MELBOURNE TO-RONTO

(215 x 138 mm.) A B–D^4(–D$_4$, which is rear pastedown endpaper); 1–7 8–26 27–30.

Contents: 1, half-title; 2, blank; 3, title page; 4, copyright page, dated 1959, with the colophon: "Printed in Great Britain by | The Windmill Press Ltd | Kingswood, Surrey"; 5, "A Visit to Morin | was first published in the *London Magazine.* | 250 copies only have been printed | and the type has been distributed"; 6, blank; 7–26, text; 27–30, blank.

Binding: Olive cloth with green silk page marker and gold lettering on spine. Dust jacket: Light parchment paper with the following on the front cover: "[all the following within a green triple-rule frame, second rule bold] GRAHAM GREENE | A Visit to Morin | HEINEMANN."

Note: Presentation copy, inscribed on recto of front free endpaper by GG to Edward Sackville–West, with his bookplate on the front pastedown endpaper. First published in *London Magazine*, 4 (January 1957), 13–25.

40. *A Burnt-out Case*

a. GRAHAM GREENE | [double rule, top rule bold] | A Burnt-Out Case | [publisher's device: Heinemann windmill] | HEINEMANN | LONDON MELBOURNE TORONTO

(196 x 128 mm.) A B–G^{16} H^4 I^{16}; *i–viii, 1–2 3–256.*

Contents: *i*, half-title; *ii*, list of books by GG; *iii*, title page; *iv*, copyright: "This English language edition first published 1961"; *v*, quotes from Dante and from R. V. Wardekar; *vi*, blank; *vii–viii*, letter, "*To Docteur Michel Lechat*" from GG; *1–256*, text.

Binding: Black cloth with silver lettering on spine. Rear board carries Heinemann windmill blind-stamped in lower right corner. Dust jacket: Front cover and spine carry a large flower in dark brown, medium brown, and blue, with author's name and title in white. Rear cover, white, carries critical excerpts on *Our Man in Havana*.

Note: First published in Sweden, translated from Greene's manuscript, as *Utbrand* (Stockholm: Norstedt, 1960), and in Denmark, as *Udbraendt* (Copenhagen: Steen Hasselbalch, 1960).

Brennan 37.

b. Uncorrected proof copy, identical to the first English edition, with these exceptions:

Contents: *iv*, copyright: "First published 1961."

Binding: Light blue paper wrappers. Front cover carries the following: "(NOT FOR SALE) | *UNCORRECTED*

PROOF COPY | [ripple rule] | A BURNT-OUT CASE | Graham Greene | [ripple rule]."

Note: Laid in loose is a one-leaf light blue mimeographed advertisement from the publisher, announcing publication for "16th January 1961."

c. *A* | *BURNT-OUT CASE* | [ripple rule] | *The Viking Press • New York • 1961* | [ripple rule] | *GRAHAM* | *GREENE*

(202 x 134 mm.) *1–8*^{16}; *i–vi* vii–viii, *1–2* 3–248.

Contents: *i*, half-title; *ii*, list of books by GG; *iii*, title page; *iv*, copyright: "Published in 1961 by The Viking Press, Inc."; *v*, quote from Dante and from R. V. Wardekar; *vi*, blank; vii–viii, letter *"To Docteur Michel Lechat"* from GG; *1*–248, text.

Binding: Pale green cloth boards with copper and green lettering on black cloth spine. Top edges stained pale green. Dust jacket: Front cover in a red, green, and black decorative pattern; within an upper white banner is title in black. Within a lower white banner is author's name in black. Spine is black with the author's name in pale green and the title in pale pink. Rear cover carries excerpts from reviews in two white banners.

Brennan 37.

41. *In Search of a Character*

a. Graham Green | IN SEARCH OF A | CHARACTER | Two African | Journals | [publisher's device: Bodley Head woodcut portrait in a single-rule frame] | THE BODLEY HEAD | LONDON

(185 x 112 mm.) *1–6*^{8} *7*^{6} *8*^{8}; *1–6* 7–9 *10–12* 13–93 *94–96* 97–123 *124*.

Contents: *1*, half-title; *2*, list of books by GG; *3*, title page; *4*, copyright: *"First published 1961"*; *5*, table of contents; *6*, blank; 7–9, Introduction; *10, blank*; *11*–123, text; *124*, blank.

Binding: Dark olive paper boards with gold lettering on orange cloth spine. Top edges stained green; dark olive and white endpapers are facsimile of a page from GG's Congo journal. Dust jacket: Yellow paper. Front cover carries the title in red and the author's name in black. Black lettering on spine.

Brennan 38.

b. Advanced unbound copy; laid in loose is a printed note, "*With the compliments of* | MAX REINHARDT | AND | THE BODLEY HEAD." Written on it is "Pub. 26th Oct | R H Elkin." Identical to the first English edition with the following exceptions:

Binding: Yellow paper wrappers with black lettering on spine. Front cover carries the following: "[simulated woodcut portrait of man, tree, and deer in upper half] | [rule] | ADVANCED UNBOUND COPY | [rule] | In Search of a Character | [double taper rule] | THE BODLEY HEAD | LONDON." Dust jacket: Identical to that of the first English edition.

c. IN | *Search* | OF A | *Character* | TWO AFRICAN JOURNALS | BY | *Graham Greene* | THE VIKING PRESS · NEW YORK

(227 x 135 mm.) $1-3^{16}$ 4^8; *i–xii* xiii–xv *xvi*, *1–2* 3–93 *94–96*.

Contents: *i*, "*This is one of 600 advance copies of* | IN SEARCH OF A CHARACTER | *specially designed for* | *friends of the author and the publishers.* | [Viking emblem] | *Christmas 1961*"; *ii*, blank; *iii*, half-title; *iv*, blank; *v*, list of Greene's works; *vi*, blank; *vii*, title page; *viii*, copyright page: "*Published in 1962 by The Viking Press, Inc.*"; *ix*, table of contents; *x*, blank; *xi–xv*, "Introduction"; *xvi*, blank; *1–93*, text; *94–96*, blank.

Binding: Pale green decorated paper boards, with gold lettering on quarter green cloth spine. Endpapers are reproductions of a page from GG's diary, with yellowish-brown background and handwriting in light tan. Wove paper, laid-paper pattern. Glassine dust jacket, as issued.

d. The trade printing, identical to the "limited edition" noted above, with the following exceptions:

Contents: *i*, Viking emblem.

Binding: Brown cloth with gold lettering on spine. Wove paper. Dust jacket: Dark green. Front cover carries author's name in white capitals in upper third, title in brown italics in middle third, and subtitle in white capitals in lower third. Spine carries the author's and publisher's names in white and the title in brown.

Brennan 38.

42. *Introductions to Three Novels*

a. Graham Greene | Introductions | to Three Novels | P. A. NORSTEDT & SÖNERS FÖRLAG | STOCKHOLM

(198 x 113 mm.) I^6 2^4 3^4 4–6^4; *1–4* 5–47 *48–52*.

Contents: *1–2*, blank; *3*, title page; *4*, copyright; 5–48, text; *49*, note on printing, in Swedish, with inscription below note: *"Norstedt's Christmas Gift Book 1962.";* *50–52*, blank.

Binding: Light gray stiff paper wrappers. Spine carries author's name in dark blue and title in red. Front cover carries the following: "[in dark blue] Graham | Greene | [in red] Introductions | to Three Novels | [in dark blue] Norstedts." Copy is unopened.

43. *21 Stories*

a. 21 Stories | by Graham Greene | [publisher's device: Viking ship] | *The Viking Press* | *New York*

(202 x 131 mm.) *1–8^{16}*; *i–iv* v–vi *vii–viii*, *1–2* 3–245 *246–248*.

Contents: *i*, half-title; *ii*, list of books by GG; *iii*, title page; *iv*, copyright: "Retitled and republished in 1962 . . ."; v–vi, table of contents; *vii*, note on first appearance of three stories; *viii*, blank; *1*, fly-title; *2*, blank; 3–245, text; *246–248*, blank.

Binding: Orange cloth with black lettering on spine. Front board carries the Viking emblem blind-stamped in lower right corner. Top edges stained orange. Dust jacket: Front cover carries erratic checkerboard design in orange, black, and light olive, with white lettering. Spine is black with white lettering. Rear cover carries a photo of GG.

44. *A Sense of Reality*

a. Graham Greene | A SENSE OF | REALITY | [publisher's device: Bodley Head woodcut portrait in a single-rule frame] | THE BODLEY HEAD | LONDON

(197 x 130 mm.) 1 $2-3^{16}$ 4^8 5^{16}; $1-8$ $9-140$ $141-144$.

Contents: 1, half-title; 2, list of books by GG; 3, title page; 4, dedication: *"To John and Gillian Sutro,"* and copyright: *"First published 1963";* 5, table of contents; 6, blank; $7-140$, text; $141-144$, blank.

Binding: Dark green cloth with gold lettering on spine. Dust jacket: Front cover is decorated in green and dark blue, with the author's name and title in the lower half on a yellow label. Spine is yellow with author's name and title in dark blue. Rear cover, white, advertises *In Search of a Character* in a single-rule green frame.

Brennan 39.

b. Uncorrected proof copy, identical to the first English edition, with these exceptions:

Contents: p. 4 lacks dedication.

Binding: Yellow paper wrappers with black lettering on spine. Front cover carries the following: "[in upper left, in blue ballpoint] 5/2 | [in upper right, in red ballpoint] Sk. | [simulated woodcut of man, tree, and deer in upper half] | [rule] | UNCORRECTED PROOF COPY | [rule] | A Sense of Reality | GRAHAM GREENE | [double taper rule] | THE BODLEY HEAD | LONDON."

c. Uncorrected proof copy, identical with the copy noted above, except that on front cover it lacks ballpoint notations in upper right and left. Instead it carries the date "21/12/62" in ballpoint in lower right corner.

d. *a* | *SENSE* | *of* | *REALITY* | GRAHAM | GREENE | [publisher's device: Viking ship] | THE VIKING PRESS NEW YORK

(202 x 133 mm.) *1–4*¹⁶; *i–viii, 1–2* 3–119 *120.*

Contents: *i*, half-title; *ii*, list of books by GG; *iii*, title page; *iv*, copyright: "*Published in 1963 by the Viking Press, Inc.*"; *v*, dedication: "*To John and Gillian Sutro*"; *vi*, blank; *vii*, table of contents; *viii*, blank; *1*–119, text; *120*, blank.

Binding: Half-tan cloth boards and spine; remainder of boards in pale blue cloth. Spine carries title, author's name, and publisher in tan on black vertical label. Front cover carries, in black, titles of stories in this collection. Top edges stained light green. Dust jacket: Front cover is decorated in black, green, and pink, with the title and author's name in white. Spine is black with green banners at the head and tail. Title and author's name are in white. Rear cover, white, carries a synopsis of each short story.

Brennan 39.

45. *The Revenge*

a. THE | REVENGE | *An autobiographical fragment by* | Graham | GREENE | PRIVATELY PRINTED | 1963

(183 x 109 mm.) *1*⁸; *1–6* 7–11 *12–16.*

Contents: *1–2*, blank; *3*, half-title; *4*, blank; *5*, title page; *6*, blank; 7–11, text; *12*, blank; *13*, colophon: "[simulated woodcut, 3 x 2 cm.: figure of medieval doctor, on left, with index finger of right hand outstretched, touching a flaming sun, on right] | Printed at the Stellar Press | in an edition of 300 copies for private | distribution by the author | and the publisher | DECEMBER | 1963; *14–16*, blank.

Binding: Stiff white paper wrappers, around which is a dark green dust jacket, stitched to the booklet at hinge. Front cover carries the following: "THE | REVENGE | An | Autobiographical | Fragment | by | GRAHAM | GREENE."

Note: First published in *Commonweal*, 61 (14 January 1955), 403–4.

46. *Carving a Statue*

a. Graham Greene | CARVING A | STATUE | A Play | [publisher's device: Bodley Head woodcut portrait in a single-rule frame] | THE BODLEY HEAD | LONDON

(184 x 111 mm.) *1* 2–4⁸ 5⁴ 6⁸; *i–ii, 1–5* 6–82 *83–86.*

Contents: *i–ii*, blank; *1*, half-title; *2*, list of books by GG; *3*, title page; *4*, copyright: *"First published 1964"; 5*, list of characters; *6*, note on first performance; 7–8, "EPI-TAPH FOR A PLAY"; 9, list of scenes and beginning of text; 10–82, text; *83–86*, blank.

Binding: Dark green cloth with gold lettering on spine. Top edges stained red; red endpapers. Dust jacket: Red; front cover shows the bottom half of a statue and scaffolding in black, with the author's name in black and the title in white in the lower half. Spine is lettered in black. Rear cover carries critical excerpts on *In Search of a Character.*

47. *The Comedians*

a. THE | Comedians | THE VIKING PRESS · NEW YORK

(280 x 138 mm.) Pp. *i–ii*, 1–219 *220–222.*

Contents: *i*, notice to reader about proofs, from Crane Duplicating Service, of Barnstable, Mass.; *ii*, blank; 1, half-title; 2, list of books by GG; 3, title page; 4, blank; 5, quote from Thomas Hardy; 6, blank; 7–8, letter to A. S. Frere; 9–219, text; *220–222*, blank.

Binding: Pale yellow paper covers, red plastic binder. Front cover carries the following: "[first line, diagonally]

UNCORRECTED PROOF | THE | Comedians | GRAHAM GREENE | [pasted on it is a pale orange sticker, 7 x 10 cm., noting publication date of 'January 28, 1965' and price of '5.00,' after which is penciled in '7⁵⁰'] | THE VIKING PRESS • NEW YORK | [in black crayon] 302."

b. THE | COMEDIANS | *Graham Greene* | THE VIKING PRESS • NEW YORK

(212 x 137 mm.) $1-10^{16}$; *i–x, 1–2 3–309 310*.

Contents: *i*, "*This is one of 500 copies of* | *the first edition of* | THE COMEDIANS | *specially bound for presentation to* | *friends of the author and the publishers* | *in advance of publication* | *Christmas 1965* [Viking emblem]"; *ii*, list of books by GG; *iii*, half-title; *iv*, blank; *v*, title page; *vi*, copyright page; *vii*, quote from Thomas Hardy; *viii*, blank; *ix–x*, letter from GG to A. S. Frere; *1–309*, text; *310*, blank.

Binding: Dark green cloth with gold lettering in two black labels on the spine. Top edges stained dark blue; tan endpapers. Glassine dust jacket, as issued.

c. THE | COMEDIANS | *Graham Greene* | THE VIKING PRESS • NEW YORK

(210 x 138 mm.) $1-10^{16}$; *i–x, 1–2 3–309 310*.

Contents: *i*, Viking emblem; *ii*, list of books by GG; *iii*, half-title; *iv*, blank; *v*, title page; *vi*, copyright: "Published in 1966 by The Viking Press, Inc."; *vii*, quote from Thomas Hardy; *viii*, blank; *ix–x*, letter to A. S. Frere; *1–309*, text; *310*, blank.

Binding: Dark green imitation leather paper boards with gold lettering on quarter black cloth spine. Top edges stained dark blue; pale green endpapers. Dust jacket: Front cover and spine are decorated in green, blue, and black. On front cover at head is a yellow sun, below which is the author's name in white and the title in yellow. In lower half are three dramatic masks, grouped together.

Spine is lettered in white and yellow. Rear cover, pale green, carries a quote from GG on Haiti.

Note: The trade printing of the "limited edition" (47b).

d. THE | COMEDIANS | Graham Greene | '. . . Aspects are within us, | and who seems | Most kingly is the King.' | *Thomas Hardy* | [publisher's device: Bodley Head woodcut portrait in single-rule frame] | THE BODLEY HEAD | LONDON

(197 x 128 mm.) B C–L^{16}; *1–4* 5–6 7–*8* 9–313 *314–320*.

Contents: *1*, half-title; *2*, list of books by GG; *3*, title page; *4*, copyright: "*First published 1966*"; *5–6*, letter to A. S. Frere; 7–313, text; *314–320*, blank.

Binding: Dark green cloth with gold lettering on spine. Top edges stained purple. Dust jacket: Olive, with a drawing of a plant, in green and blue, extending across lower half of the jacket. Author's name and title are in white on the front cover and spine.

48. *Victorian Detective Fiction*

a. VICTORIAN | DETECTIVE FICTION | [ornamental rule] | A CATALOGUE OF THE COLLECTION MADE BY | DOROTHY GLOVER & GRAHAM GREENE | BIBLIOGRAPHICALLY ARRANGED | BY ERIC OSBORNE AND | INTRODUCED BY JOHN CARTER | [Bodley Head woodcut portrait in olive ink in an oval frame] | WITH A PREFACE BY | GRAHAM GREENE | THE BODLEY HEAD · LONDON | SYDNEY & TORONTO

(248 x 158 mm.) *A* B–H^8 I^4 K^8 L^{10}; *i–vi* vii–xv *xvi* xvii–xviii *xix–xx*, 1–149 *150–152*.

Contents: *i*, half-title; *ii*, blank; *iii*, title page; *iv*, copyright page; *v*, table of contents; *vi*, blank; vii–viii, preface by GG; ix–xv, introduction by John Carter; *xvi*, blank; xvii–xviii, compiler's note by Osborne; *xix*, half-title: "The Catalogue"; *xx*, blank; 1–121, the catalogue; *122*, blank; 123–126, appendix on publishing history of *The Mystery of a Hansom Cab; 127*, note on endpapers; *128*, blank; *129–136*, index of detectives; *137–140*, index of illustrators; *141–149*, index of titles; *150*, blank; *151*, colophon: "*Printed in Ehrhardt types | at The Stellar Press in Barnet, Herts, | by Bill Hummerstone on Strathmore mould-made | paper and bound by Wm. Clowes at Beccles. | The edition is limited to 500 copies | (of which 25 copies are not for sale) and signed by | Dorothy Glover, Graham Greene | and John Carter. | No. 77 |* [signed] Dorothy Glover | [signed] Graham Greene | PRINTED IN GREAT BRITAIN | [signed] John Carter"; *152*, blank.

Binding: Dark green cloth with gold lettering on spine. Top edges stained pale green. Endpapers are reproductions in white on gray of two drawings by Millais based on an unlocated story, "The Captain and the Detective." Laid paper. Dust jacket: Olive laid paper with the following on the front cover: "[in blue ink] VICTORIAN | DE-TECTIVE | FICTION | [in black ink] A CATALOGUE | OF THE COLLECTION | MADE BY | DOROTHY GLOVER & | GRAHAM GREENE | [Bodley Head woodcut portrait in blue ink in an oval frame]." Spine is lettered in blue.

49. *May We Borrow Your Husband?*

a. Graham Greene | May We Borrow | Your Husband? | *And Other Comedies of | the Sexual Life | Cling to the virtues normally | manifested by all Lebanese. |* Prime Minister Sami-as-Suhl | [publisher's device: Bodley Head woodcut portrait in a single-rule frame] | THE BODLEY HEAD | LONDON SYDNEY | TORONTO

(197 x 128 mm.) 1^{16} (1_2+1) $2–6^{16}$; *i–ii, 1–8* 9–188 *189–192.*

Contents: *i*, half-title; *ii*, list of books by GG; *1*, title page; *2*, copyright page; *3*, "Of this book | first published in April 1967 | a numbered edition of 500 copies | has been specially printed | and bound and signed | by Gra-ham Greene | THIS IS NUMBER | 113 | [signed] Graham Greene"; *4*, blank; *5*, table of contents; *6*, blank; *7*, half-title; *8*, blank; *9–188*, text; *189–192*, blank.

Binding: Decorated green and light green paper boards with gold lettering on quarter green cloth spine. Top edges stained pale purple; endpapers tan, with laid-paper design. Glassine dust jacket, as issued.

b. A copy of the first trade publication, identical to the "limited edition" (49a) with these exceptions:

(197 x 128 mm.) *1* 2–6¹⁶; *1–8* 9–188 *189–192*.

Contents: *1*, half-title; *2*, list of books by GG; *3*, title page; *4–192*, identical to limited edition.

Binding: Dark green cloth with gold lettering on spine. Top edges stained purple. Dust jacket: Pictorial front cover, in white, pink, black, red, and yellow, shows a small table and three chairs under a palm tree, in front of the wall of a house. Author's name appears in a red label with yellow and red border. Title is white in a black label. Spine is pink, with black lettering. Rear cover, white, carries critical excerpts on *The Comedians*.

c. [title page on pp. iv–v; on p. iv:] *Graham Greene* | [rule] | Cling to the virtues normally manifested by all Lebanese. | — Prime Minister Sami-as-Sulh | [on p. v:] *May We Borrow* | *Your Husband?* | [rule] | AND OTHER COMEDIES | OF THE SEXUAL LIFE | NEW YORK / THE VIKING PRESS |

(212 x 131 mm.) *1–6¹⁶*; *i–viii, 1–2* 3–183 *184*.

Contents: *i*, half-title; *ii*, blank; *iii*, list of books by GG; *iv–v*, title page; *vi*, copyright: "Published in 1967 by The Viking Press, Inc."; *vii*, table of contents; *viii*, blank; *1*, fly-title; *2*, blank; *3–183*, text; *184*, blank.

Binding: Olive paper boards with gold lettering on quarter black cloth spine. Front board carries initials "GG" in gold. Top edges stained light green; olive endpapers. Dust jacket: Front cover carries in upper half a black background on which are the author's name in white, the main title in orange, and the subtitle in green; in lower half, on a white background, are two reversed interlocking capital G's, the left G green, the right G orange, with a black asterisk within the interlocking part of the capitals. Spine is orange with the author's and publisher's names in black and the title in white. Rear cover, white, carries an excerpt from the story "Two Gentle People."

50. *Collected Essays*

   a. Graham Greene | Collected Essays | [publisher's device: Bodley Head woodcut portrait in a single-rule frame] | THE BODLEY HEAD | LONDON SYDNEY | TORONTO

   (197 x 130 mm.) *1* 2–29⁸; *1–4* 5–10 *11–12* 13–463 *464*.

   Contents: *1*, half-title; *2*, list of books by GG; *3*, title page; *4*, copyright: *"First Published 1969"*; *5–8*, table of contents; *9*, "Author's Note"; *10*, "Acknowledgments"; *11–463*, text; *464*, blank.

   Binding: Dark green cloth with gold lettering on spine. Top edges stained pale purple. Dust jacket: Front cover is gray; author's name appears in white in upper half, below which is a bluish green band 5 mm. wide. In lower half is title in black. Spine is white with black and bluish-green lettering. Rear cover, white, carries critical quotes on *The Lost Childhood.*

   b. Graham Greene | Collected Essays | [ornamental calligraphic parallelogram, 19 x 12 mm.] | NEW YORK / THE VIKING PRESS

   (196 x 130 mm.) *1–7*¹⁶ *8*⁸ *9–15*¹⁶; *1–4* 5–10 *11–12* 13–463 *464*.

   Contents: Identical to the first English edition, except that copyright p. *4* carries the note, "Published in 1969 by The Viking Press, Inc."

   Binding: Half-orange cloth boards and spine; remainder of boards are pale brown cloth. Spine is lettered in black, with gold calligraphic parallelogram. Top edges stained orange. Dust jacket: Front cover and spine are black, with author's name in white and title in gold on both. Lower third of each carries a colored geometrical design in a white frame. Rear cover, white, carries a note on the essays, and the same geometrical design appears in lower third, in a single-rule gold frame.

Note: The American publication is a separate printing of the first English edition, with a differing imposition of pages and with variant title and copyright pages.

51. *Travels with My Aunt*

a. TRAVELS | WITH MY AUNT | *A NOVEL* | Graham Greene | [publisher's device: Bodley Head woodcut portrait in a single-rule frame] | THE BODLEY HEAD | LONDON SYDNEY | TORONTO

(197 x 130 mm.) 1^{16} 2–10^{16}; *1–8* 9–319 *320*.

Contents: *1*, half-title; *2*, list of books by GG; *3*, title page; *4*, copyright: *"First published 1969"*; *5*, dedication: "FOR H. H. K. | who helped me more | than I can tell"; *6*, blank; 7, half-title for Part I; *8*, blank; 9–319, text; *320*, blank.

Binding: Dark green cloth with gold lettering on spine. Top edges stained green. Dust jacket: White paper. Front cover carries author's name and title at head in black ink. Below, at left, is a pictorial representation of a bell jar containing a fountain and doves, in blue, red, and black; and at right is a potted orange dahlia. At tail are four geometric blocks in red, blue, yellow, and green. Spine carries the author's name and title in black ink. Rear cover, white, carries critical excerpts on *Collected Essays* in black.

b. [title printed across pages *iv* and *v*; on p. *iv:*] A novel by | [two intertwined scrolled lines] | *GRAHAM GREENE* | [on p. *v:*] *TRAVELS* | *WITH MY AUNT* | *NEW YORK* / *THE VIKING PRESS*

(210 x 145 mm.) *1–8*^{16}; *i–viii, 1–2* 3–244 *245–248*.

Contents: *i*, half-title; *ii*, blank; *iii*, list of books by GG; *iv–v*, title page; *vi*, copyright: "Published in 1970 by The Viking Press, Inc."; *vii*, dedication: "FOR H. H. K. | who helped me more | than I can tell"; *viii*, blank; *1*, half-title for Part I; *2*, blank; *3–244*, text; *245–248*, blank.

Binding: Purple paper boards. Spine is lettered in purple, with gold design, on quarter pale gray cloth. The front board carries two gold italic lowercase G's stamped in the lower right quarter. Top edges stained purple; purple endpapers. Fore edges and tail uncut. Dust jacket: Front cover and spine are light purple paper. Front cover carries author's name in black at head and title in blue at center. At tail is an illustration of a bell jar containing a bird and flowers in white and blue and red, and a red potted dahlia. Spine is lettered in white and black. Rear cover, white, carries a black potted dahlia at head and an excerpt from Chapter I below it.

52. *A Sort of Life*

a. A | SORT | OF | LIFE | [rule] | Graham Greene | [rule] | [publisher's device: Bodley Head woodcut portrait in a single-rule frame] | THE BODLEY HEAD | LONDON SYDNEY | TORONTO

(196 x 128 mm.) *1* 2–7^{16}; *i–ii*, *1–8* 9–215 *216–222*.

Contents: *i–ii*, blank; *1*, half-title; *2*, list of books by GG; *3*, title page; *4*, copyright: *"First published 1971"*; *5*, dedication: *"For the survivors,* | *Raymond Greene, Hugh Greene* | *and Elisabeth Dennys"*; *6*, blank; *7*, quote from Søren Kierkegaard; *8*, blank; *9–10*, author's note on scope and purpose of the book; *11–216*, text; *217–222*, blank.

Binding: Green cloth with gold lettering on spine. Top edges stained green. Dust jacket: Dark purple paper. Front cover carries the following: "[in white] Graham Greene | [bold pink rule] | [in pale orange] A | SORT | OF | LIFE." Spine carries author's name in pale orange, title in white, and publisher in pink.

b. A | SORT | OF LIFE | [rule] | GRAHAM GREENE | SIMON AND SCHUSTER | NEW YORK

(210 x 135 mm.) $1-7^{16}$; $1-10$ 11–220 $221-224$.

Contents: *1*, publisher's device: Simon and Schuster's emblem of The Sower; *2–3*, list of books by GG; *4*, blank; *5*, title page; *6*, copyright: "1971 by Graham Greene | Published by Simon and Schuster"; 7, dedication: "For the Survivors, | Raymond Greene, | Hugh Greene | and | Elisabeth Dennys"; *8*, blank; *9*, quote from Kierkegaard; *10*, blank; 11–12, author's note on the scope and purpose of the book; 13–220, text; *221–224*, blank.

Binding: Black cloth with silver lettering on spine. Gray endpapers. Dust jacket: Front cover is white paper with author's name at head and title at tail, all printed in black within a double-rule frame, outer rule bold and dark red and inner rule narrow and red. Spine is white with author's name in black, title in red, and publisher in dark red. Rear cover carries Karsh's portrait of GG.

53. *The Pleasure-Dome*

a. THE | PLEASURE- | DOME | Graham Greene | The Collected Film Criticism 1935–1940 | Edited by John Russell Taylor | *'It was a miracle of rare device,* | *A sunny pleasure-dome with caves of ice.'* | Secker & Warburg | London

(244 x 170 mm.) $1-18^{8}$; *i–iv*, 1–284.

Contents: *i*, half-title; *ii*, black-and-white photo of GG; *iii*, title page; *iv*, copyright: "First published in England 1972"; 1–275, text; 276–277, note on GG's libelous review of *Wee Willie Winkie;* 278–284, Index.

Binding: Black cloth with silver lettering on spine. Endpapers carry a black-and-white photo of a theater interior tinted a fluorescent pale pink. Dust jacket: Gray background carries a photographic representation of a theater interior in black on the front cover and spine; author's name is in white and title is in pink on both. Rear cover carries, on one-third of the right side, part of the photo on front cover and spine; remainder carries a list of film reviews.

b. The American publication, identical to the English, with these exceptions:

Title page: GRAHAM GREENE | ON | FILM | Collected Film Criticism 1935–1940 | Edited by John Russell Taylor | SIMON AND SCHUSTER | New York

Contents: p. *i*, Simon and Schuster's emblem of The Sower; p. *iv*, "First U.S. printing."

Dust jacket: Black, with title on front cover in white within a film-projection gold, single-line frame. Spine has red and white lettering. Rear cover carries Karsh's portrait of GG.

54. *The Honorary Consul*

a. THE HONORARY | CONSUL | [double-taper rule, 2 cm.] | Graham Greene | 'All things merge in one another— | good into evil, generosity into | justice, religion into politics . . .' | *Thomas Hardy* | [publisher's device: Bodley Head woodcut portrait in an oval frame] | THE BODLEY HEAD | LONDON SYDNEY | TORONTO

(191 x 122 mm.) *1–9*^{16} *10*^{8} *11*^{16}; *1–8 9–334 335–336.*

Contents: *1*, half-title; *2*, list of books by GG; *3*, title page; *4*, disclaimer and copyright: *"First Published 1973"*; *5*, dedication to Victoria Ocampo; *6*, blank; *7–335*, text; *336*, blank.

Binding: Dark green cloth with gold lettering on spine. Top edges stained dark green. Dust jacket: Front and rear covers are black with white borders, carrying author's name in upper half in blue and title in lower half in pale green. Spine is white with author's name in blue and title in black.

b. THE | HONORARY | CONSUL | [rule] | GRAHAM GREENE | [rule] | SIMON AND SCHUSTER | NEW YORK

(233 x 156 mm.) *1–10*^{16}; *1–14 15–315 316–320.*

Contents: *1*, Simon and Schuster's emblem of The Sower; *2–3*, list of books by GG; *4*, blank; *5*, title page; *6*, copyright page; *7*, disclaimer; *8*, blank; *9*, dedication to Victoria Ocampo; *10*, blank; *11*, quote from Thomas Hardy; *12*, blank; *13–315*, text; *316–320*, blank.

Binding: Dark blue cloth with gold lettering on spine. Dust jacket: Front cover and spine are orange in upper half, fading to yellow in lower half. In upper third of front cover is the author's name in black; lower two-thirds carries a single-rule frame, with title at the bottom in black. Spine has black lettering. Rear cover, white, carries Karsh's portrait of GG.

55. *Lord Rochester's Monkey*

a. *Graham Greene* | [in calligraphic flourishes] *Lord Rochester's Monkey* | *being the Life of John Wilmot,* | *Second Earl of Rochester* | *Bodley Head* | *London • Sydney • Toronto*

(248 x 185 mm.) *1–13*[8]; *1–8 9–231 232*. Color plates before pp. 2, 21, 183, 201; two color plates each before pp. 65, 101, 137, 157. Plates are counted in pagination but not numbered.

Contents: *1*, color reproduction of painting in oval gold frame; *2*, color portrait of Rochester; *3*, title page; *4*, copyright; *5*, two quotes from Rochester; *6*, blank; *7*, table of contents; *8*, list of plates; *9–11*, "Preface"; *12*, black-and-white reproduction of portraits of Rochester's parents; *13–221*, text; *222–223*, "Bibliography"; *224–226*, "Illustrations and Acknowledgements"; *226–231*, Index; *232*, blank.

Binding: Brown cloth with gold lettering on spine. Top edges stained pale yellow; endpapers carry a black-and-white reproduction of a painting of the Restoration of King Charles. Dust jacket: Front cover carries a color portrait of Rochester, with the author's name and title in white. Spine is deep reddish-brown, lettered in white. Rear cover, deep reddish-brown, carries a facsimile of a Rochester poem in his hand.

b. Another copy, the American publication, identical to the English with the following exceptions:

Title page reads "*A Studio Book* | *The Viking Press* • *New York*" in place of the last two lines of the English title page. Copyright page varies extensively but is dated 1974. Tails of spine on binding and dust jacket carry "*Viking*" in place of "Bodley Head."

56. *The Return of A. J. Raffles*

a. Graham Greene | [device: parallelogram, 1 x 25 mm.] | THE RETURN OF | A. J. RAFFLES | An Edwardian Comedy | in Three Acts based somewhat loosely | on E. W. Hornung's characters in | *The Amateur Cracksman* | [publisher's device: Bodley Head woodcut portrait in an oval frame] | THE BODLEY HEAD | LONDON SYDNEY | TORONTO

(191 x 116 mm.) *1–5*^{8}; *1–8* 9–79 *80*.

Contents: *1*, half-title; *2*, list of books by GG; *3*, title page; *4*, copyright: "*First published 1975*"; *5*, Author's Note; *6*, blank; *7*, list of characters; *8*, blank; *9–80*, text.

Binding: Stiff gray paper wrappers. Spine carries the title in red and the author's name in deep purple. Front cover carries, in upper half, title in red, below which is a deep yellow bar; lower half carries author's name in deep purple capitals. Rear cover carries, in deep purple and red, an advertisement for the Collected Edition of GG's works.

Note: This title was also issued in a "limited edition" of 250 copies bound in boards, of which nos. 81–250 were offered for sale. Copy examined: Lilly PR6013.R4R43, copy 1 (no. 195).

57. *The Human Factor*

a. THE HUMAN | FACTOR | [double taper rule] | Graham Greene | 'I only know that he who forms a tie is lost. The | germ of corruption has entered into his soul.' | *Joseph Conrad* | [Bodley Head woodcut portrait in oval frame] | THE BODLEY HEAD | LONDON SYDNEY | TORONTO

(197 x 127 mm.) *1–9*[16] *10*[10] *11*[16]; *1–8 9–338 339–340.*

Contents: *1*, half-title; *2*, list of books by GG; *3*, title page; *4*, author's disclaimer in upper half and copyright in lower half: *"First published 1978"; 5*, dedication to Elisabeth Dennys; *6*, blank; 7, "PART I"; *8*, blank; *9–339*, text; *340*, blank.

Binding: Dark green cloth with gold lettering on spine. Top edges stained dark green. Dust jacket: White paper. Front cover carries in upper two-thirds the title printed diagonally in brown outline letters. Superimposed over title is the author's name in red capitals. Title is repeated in lower third in brown letters. Spine is lettered in brown and red. Rear cover carries same design as front, but author's name is in dark blue capitals.

b. Graham Greene | [bold rule] | THE | HUMAN | FAC-TOR | [Simon and Schuster emblem: the sower] | Simon and Schuster • New York

(234 x 142 mm.) *1–11*[16]; *1–14 15–347 348–352.*

Contents: *1*, Simon and Schuster emblem: the sower; *2–3*, list of books by GG; *4*, blank; *5*, title page; *6*, copyright: *"1978 by Graham Greene"*; 7, author's disclaimer; *8*, blank; *9*, dedication to Elisabeth Dennys; *10*, blank; *11*, quote from Joseph Conrad; *12*, blank; *13–347*, text; *348– 352*, blank.

Binding: Black cloth with silver lettering on spine. Red endpapers. Dust jacket: front cover gray, carries the following: "[in red] GRAHAM | GREENE | [in white] A NOVEL | [on the left side, halfway down, a parklike scene in green, dark brown, and bluish gray], [on the same line, in black] THE | HUMAN | FACTOR." Rear cover and spine are black, with spine lettered in red, white, and blue. Rear cover carries Karsh portrait of GG.

Note: *The Human Factor* was also issued in a limited edition through the Franklin Library series (letter from Anthony Rota of Bertram Rota, Ltd.).

INDEX

Reference is to catalog listing, not page number.

About the Author

Robert H. Miller is professor of English and chairman of the Division of Humanities at the University of Louisville.

12.00

G.